INDIANS

POCAHONTAS, *Seymour*
PONTIAC, *Peckham*
SACAGAWEA, *Seymour*
SEQUOYAH, *Snow*
SITTING BULL, *Stevenson*
SQUANTO, *Stevenson*
TECUMSEH, *Stevenson*

NAVAL HEROES

DAVID FARRAGUT, *Long*
GEORGE DEWEY, *Long*
JOHN PAUL JONES, *Snow*
MATTHEW CALBRAITH PERRY, *Scharbach*
OLIVER HAZARD PERRY, *Long*
RAPHAEL SEMMES, *Snow*
STEPHEN DECATUR, *Smith*

NOTED WIVES and MOTHERS

ABIGAIL ADAMS, *Wagoner*
DOLLY MADISON, *Monsell*
JESSIE FREMONT, *Wagoner*
MARTHA WASHINGTON, *Wagoner*
MARY TODD LINCOLN, *Wilkie*
NANCY HANKS, *Stevenson*
RACHEL JACKSON, *Govan*

SCIENTISTS and INVENTORS

ALBERT EINSTEIN, *Hammontree*
ALECK BELL, *Widdemer*
CYRUS MCCORMICK, *Dobler*
ELIAS HOWE, *Corcoran*
ELI WHITNEY, *Snow*
ELIZABETH BLACKWELL, *Henry*
GEORGE CARVER, *Stevenson*
GEORGE EASTMAN, *Henry*
HENRY FORD, *Aird and Ruddiman*
JOHN AUDUBON, *Mason*
LUTHER BURBANK, *Burt*
MARIA MITCHELL, *Melin*
ROBERT FULTON, *Henry*
SAMUEL MORSE, *Snow*
TOM EDISON, *Guthridge*
WALTER REED, *Higgins*
WILBUR AND ORVILLE WRIGHT, *Stevenson*
WILL AND CHARLIE MAYO, *Hammontree*

SOCIAL and CIVIC

...N,
...on

FRANCES WILLARD, *Mason*
JANE ADDAMS, *Wagoner*
JOHN L. LEWIS, *Korson*
J. STERLING MORTON, *Moore*
JULIA WARD HOWE, *Wagoner*
JULIETTE LOW, *Higgins*
LILIUOKALANI, *Newman*
LUCRETIA MOTT, *Burnett*
MOLLY PITCHER, *Stevenson*
OLIVER WENDELL HOLMES, JR., *Dunham*
SUSAN ANTHONY, *Monsell*

SOLDIERS

ANTHONY WAYNE, *Stevenson*
BEDFORD FORREST, *Parks*
DAN MORGAN, *Bryant*
ETHAN ALLEN, *Winders*
FRANCIS MARION, *Steele*
ISRAEL PUTNAM, *Stevenson*
JEB STUART, *Winders*
NATHANAEL GREENE, *Peckham*
ROBERT E. LEE, *Monsell*
SAM HOUSTON, *Stevenson*
TOM JACKSON, *Monsell*
U. S. GRANT, *Stevenson*
WILLIAM HENRY HARRISON, *Peckham*
ZACK TAYLOR, *Wilkie*

STATESMEN

ABE LINCOLN, *Stevenson*
ANDY JACKSON, *Stevenson*
DAN WEBSTER, *Smith*
FRANKLIN ROOSEVELT, *Weil*
HENRY CLAY, *Monsell*
JAMES MONROE, *Widdemer*
JEFF DAVIS, *de Grummond and Delaune*
JOHN MARSHALL, *Monsell*
TEDDY ROOSEVELT, *Parks*
WOODROW WILSON, *Monsell*

J. Sterling Morton

Morton

Arbor Day Boy

Illustrated by Robert Doremus

J. Sterling Morton

Morton

Arbor Day Boy

By Clyde B. Moore

THE **BOBBS-MERRILL** COMPANY, INC.
A SUBSIDIARY OF HOWARD W. SAMS & CO., INC.
Publishers • INDIANAPOLIS • NEW YORK

To the children of America

Illustrations

Full pages	PAGE
"What's that?" asked Sterling.	19
"Your stunt added to the fun."	34
To be in the pilot house was wonderful.	63
He saw a bin of crawling creatures.	78
The two boys stood watching.	109
"Do you see how it works?"	124
Sterling led the way along the train.	141
The boys looked at the seats.	144
Sterling remembered the rules.	167
Sterling Morton planted a tree.	190

Numerous smaller illustrations

Contents

PAGE

Howdy, Stranger   11
Frontier Birthday Party   24
Steamboats on Lake Erie   38
Off to New York   52
Frontier Boy in
   New York City   71
School Days   89

PAGE

Uncle Edward's
   Print Shop   103
Coming of the Railroad   118
The First Train   132
Early Teens   148
To Boarding School   158
West to the Prairies   173
Arbor Day   183

CHILDHOOD

OF FAMOUS

AMERICANS

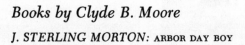

Books by Clyde B. Moore

J. STERLING MORTON: ARBOR DAY BOY

★ J. Sterling Morton

Arbor Day Boy

Howdy, Stranger

It was the spring of 1834. The Morton family had left their home in Adams, New York, to go west. Two-year-old Sterling had been tucked in with all the family belongings.

Now the belongings, the family, and young Sterling were a part of Monroe, Michigan, on the shore of Lake Erie.

As the years slipped by, Sterling caught the spirit of the growing frontier town. He was growing up.

"Mother," Sterling would say, "that new store is going to be a whopper. It will be the biggest building in town."

According to his mother, Sterling "grew up like a weed."

Large for his age and always curious Sterling would say, "I just want to see everything."

Sterling was really an early explorer of the growing village and countryside. New settlers arrived nearly every day, and Sterling and his friends were on hand to see them.

Families from the East were moving to the West. Many families settled in Monroe. Other families pushed on farther. Some people were on their way to the prairie lands west of the Mississippi River.

To Sterling all this activity was very exciting. Something new happened every day. He loved to listen to the stories of the travelers. Sometimes he wished he might go on with them to the far, far West. Sterling never grew tired of watching the great covered wagons as they rolled slowly on their way.

Day after day the wagons came by. They were loaded with farming tools and home furnishings and families.

At the front of the prairie schooner or covered wagon sat the father, the driver of the horses. Sterling liked to listen to the driver urge the horses to keep going.

The mother sat beside the father. She often turned to the children who were perched on the family belongings behind her. Blankets spread over the family belongings made a wonderful place for the young travelers.

The sides of the canvas cover could be lifted like a curtain. This delighted the children. They could then look out as the wagon moved slowly along the street.

"What do you think?" said Sterling one day. "We boys have counted the travelers passing through for ten days. There were more than all the people living in Monroe."

Whenever possible Sterling would ask where the people were going and from where they had come. Some were on their way to Iowa and Nebraska. Others planned to go all the way to California or Oregon. They seemed to have come from every state in the East.

These travelers thrilled Sterling. He did not know how far away these places were, but he knew it to be a long, long way. He wondered if he might some day go farther west.

Sterling liked best to see the families that came to settle in Monroe. Sterling was always eager to know if there were boys of his age in the new family. He liked people.

Sterling and his young friends watched to see what the new families brought with them. What was more fun than to see the "movings" the people brought?

Sterling heard the men of Monroe as they talked to strangers. It was the same for the

14

settlers as for those who were passing through the town.

Sterling liked to hear them say, "Howdy, stranger!" He could say it to new boys just as the men did to men. It seemed so friendly and a good way to start talking.

One morning in April, 1840, Sterling met a new boy. He liked his pleasant smile. The boy was taller than Sterling and perhaps a little older. A pair of bright blue eyes looked out from under a shock of red hair. Those eyes seemed fairly to twinkle. Freckles were sprinkled across his nose.

Sterling liked him at once and said, "Howdy, stranger. Where did you used to live?"

"Howdy," came the response. "I'm from Connecticut. What's your name?"

"Sterling Morton. What's yours?"

"John Bradford, but most people call me Jack," the new boy answered.

That was the way frontier boys became acquainted with each other. The two boys shook hands as they had so often seen men do when strangers met.

"Where do you live?" asked Sterling.

"In that house," explained Jack, pointing down the street. "It is near that carpenter shop."

"Oh, I have been over there many times!" exclaimed Sterling. "That is Sam Wood's carpenter shop. He gives me little blocks of wood and lets me catch the shavings when he planes a board. When he planes a board, it is smooth as silk. The shavings are like ribbons."

Jack was impressed. "Does he like boys?"

"Oh, sure," said Sterling. "He has some of his own. Mrs. Wood is nice, too."

The boys were no longer strangers.

"Come on over, Sterling," suggested Jack, "and see our movings. They are not in place yet. It is fun to see them stacked around anywhere."

The two boys trudged along the way, talking as they went.

Sterling had dozens of questions to ask about Connecticut. He had heard about it and knew it had a shore on the Atlantic Ocean.

"Have you seen the ocean?" asked Sterling.

"Yes, several times. We lived near Hartford, but my grandfather lived near the shore. We used to go there in the summer."

"I wish I could see the ocean," mused Sterling.

The boys had now reached the Bradford home. The furnishings or movings were stacked about all higgledy-piggledy.

"This is my new friend, Sterling Morton," said Jack to his mother.

Mrs. Bradford put out her hand and said, "I am glad to meet you, Sterling."

She said it in such a friendly way that Sterling thought he knew why Jack had been so friendly when they first met.

"You boys may look at the movings, but be careful not to break anything," cautioned Mrs. Bradford. "Remember do not get in the way of your father or me. We are busy putting things in place."

The boys said they would be careful and would not get in the way.

Sterling and Jack were amused by the strange way things were packed. A small mirror rested with its face on a pillow. The pillow was tucked into a large kettle. The mirror had ridden all the way from Connecticut without a crack.

"What is that?" asked Sterling, pointing to something rolled in heavy blankets. It was longer than a man. With all the blankets it was big enough to be a giant.

"That is a clock," answered Jack. "It is called a grandfather clock. It was made by Seth Thomas in his shop at Plymouth Hollow. That is a town in Connecticut."

"You mean it was made in Connecticut?" asked Sterling.

"That's right. I did not see this one made, but my father took me to see the shop."

"It must be a huge clock," Sterling commented thoughtfully. "I hope I can see it when it is placed and running. I have heard Grandfather Morton tell about those clocks. He said Seth Thomas knew more about how to make clocks than anybody in New England."

The boys continued to explore.

They gave a turn to the coffee grinder. Green coffee beans were then roasted and ground in the home kitchen.

Sterling lifted a big flatiron. "This is the heaviest flatiron I have ever seen," he said. "It must take a hot fire to heat it."

No one, as yet, had even dreamed of an electric iron, nor an electric light for that matter.

Sterling examined the candle molds very carefully. Jack explained how the wick was placed in the mold first. Then the hot tallow was poured in to harden around it.

The boys now came to the butter churn. Sterling knew what that was. He had often watched his mother make butter.

This churn was made of wood. It looked as if it were a tall bucket turned upside down. There was a hole in the cover for the handle of the dasher to pass through. Sometimes Sterling helped his mother by working the dasher up and down, up and down, through the thick cream until butter was made.

"Have you ever had a drink of fresh buttermilk?" asked Sterling.

"Sure," answered Jack, "many times."

Sterling then looked at the great wooden bowl in which the butter was "worked". Both boys had seen their mothers work the butter with a wooden paddle.

Sterling had watched his mother press the butter against the side of the bowl to squeeze out the water and milk. She would then form the butter into a great roll and put it in a cool place to keep fresh.

The boys examined the spinning wheel, a loom for weaving, the andirons for the fireplace, the tables, and the chairs.

Sterling had enjoyed seeing all the movings. Now it was time for him to go.

He thanked Mrs. Bradford and started home. It had been a good day. He had a found a new friend. Sterling was sure they would have many good times together.

Sterling walked slowly to his home. He thought of the new houses that were being built. Monroe was growing larger every day as new settlers came. He was very proud of his town's rapid growth.

He stopped to look at a new store. It was almost finished. Mr. Wood had made these counters and shelves in his shop.

Sterling peeked inside. He could see great boxes and bales of goods. He could hardly wait for the store to open for business.

Sterling was almost home.

Suddenly he stopped short.

Then he dashed into the house. "Mother," he shouted, "I have a wonderful idea for my birthday party."

Frontier
Birthday Party

NO BOY IN Michigan was more active than Sterling Morton. Always on the go, he was a natural explorer of the country.

Of course he was not a real early explorer who swam rivers and fought Indians. He did not live on bear meat and wild berries. Sterling just wanted to learn everything he could about the frontier.

Sterling and his friends explored everything in sight. They roamed through the woods, up the streams, and about the town. Sterling knew the names of all the trees in the woods as well as he knew the people in the town.

His young friends often came trooping into the Morton home. Sterling's mother seemed to understand boys. She liked the boys, and the boys like Mrs. Morton.

One reason may have been that she kept a big jar well filled with cookies. That is, it was well filled until the boys came. Then down went the level in the cooky jar, and down went the cookies into the stomachs of the young explorers.

This was the way things were when Sterling dashed into the house with his big idea.

"Mother," he exclaimed, "I have just found a wonderful friend. His name is Jack Bradford. The Bradfords have come from Connecticut."

Sterling seemed fairly bursting with news. He could not tell it fast enough.

"Just a minute, my boy," interrupted his mother, with a chuckle. Sterling's bursts of enthusiasm often amused her. "How do you know so much about the Bradfords?"

Sterling slowed down for a moment.

Then excitedly he told of his visit to the Bradford home. He told of the grandfather clock, the candle-molds, and all the rest. He and Jack had had a wonderful time. Jack's mother had been very friendly, too.

Mrs. Morton could see that Sterling was greatly pleased over this new family.

Sterling talked on and on. . Then Mrs. Morton asked, "But what was your big idea? You dashed in here like a cyclone. You were bursting to tell it."

Sterling blushed. "Oh, I forgot. It was about my birthday. You said for my eighth birthday I could have two of my friends to supper."

"Yes," replied his mother. "You said you would like Frank and Ted. I have invited them."

"Well, Mother, I did not know Jack then. He is really a brand-new neighbor. I do wish he could come."

Mrs. Morton smiled. What was better for her fiery young son than to be a good neighbor?

Her face was thoughtful. She had not planned a big birthday party. Grandfather Morton and Uncle Edward would come to supper. It was to be a simple family affair.

Then turning to Sterling she said, "I think your idea is excellent. You may invite him."

"May I go right over and invite him?"

"I think you should wait until tomorrow morning. We can talk it over with your father when he comes home. He should be here soon."

She had hardly spoken when in walked Julius Morton, Sterling's father.

Now Sterling's father was a stern man. He was pleased to see his son so strong and active. But Sterling had managed to get into a few scrapes that did not please his father.

"Go ahead and tell your father of your new idea," urged his mother.

His father looked puzzled as if he wondered what might have happened. Had Sterling been in trouble again?

Sterling understood all this. He also felt sure that his father would approve this idea if he could explain it.

Sterling told of meeting Jack. He told of the things he saw at the Bradford home. He explained how well they were packed. Nothing had been broken during the long journey. His father showed great interest in the grandfather clock. At the end Sterling explained, "I have asked mother if I may invite Jack to my birthday supper. She thinks it is a good idea, but that I should ask you, too."

When Sterling had finished, his father said, "That is a very good idea. Everyone should be a good neighbor."

Breakfast finished, the next morning, Sterling Morton was off to the home of Jack Bradford.

When he knocked, Mrs. Bradford came to the door. She greeted the young caller with a smile.

"Good morning, Sterling. You are out bright and early this fine morning. I suppose you want to see Jack."

"Yes," said Sterling, "but I want to see you, too. Tomorrow is my birthday. I want Jack to come to supper. My mother said I may invite him if you approve."

"Of course I approve," said Mrs. Morton as she turned to call Jack. "Jack, Sterling is here to see you." The she asked Sterling, "How old will you be?"

"I'll be eight tomorrow," Sterling replied.

Jack hurried in.

"Good morning, Sterling."

"Jack, I came to invite you to my birthday supper, tomorrow. My mother said I may ask you, and your mother says you may come."

Jack smiled. His eyes twinkled, and his

freckled nose showed little wrinkles. He was greatly pleased.

"Wonderful!" said Jack.

"Frank Caldwall and Ted Davis are coming," explained Sterling. "You will like them."

So it was planned for Sterling's birthday.

The great day came with a flood of warm sunshine. It was April 22. Sterling did not then know that years later that would be a very important date to thousands of people.

No one called Sterling that morning. Perhaps the excitement of a birthday awakened him. He bounced out of bed like a jack-in-the-box. On went his clothes, and down the stairs he hurried.

"Happy birthday," called his mother. Other members of the family chimed in.

"So you are eight years old," said his father. "Come right over here and let me give you a good spanking."

30

Sterling knew what was coming. A spanking on his birthday was an honor.

His father counted, "One, two, three, four, five, six, seven, eight, and one to grow on."

Everybody laughed—including Sterling.

His mother had prepared his favorite breakfast. There were golden brown griddle cakes and maple syrup.

What was this neat package at his plate?

"That is a gift from your Grandfather Morton," explained Sterling's father. "He thinks a young woodsman like you should be equipped."

Sterling opened the package with great care. Out popped a pocket knife such as hunters and woodsmen carried. The brown stag handle just fitted his hand. The blades were bright as silver.

"Those blades are very sharp," warned his father. "Always be careful in handling a knife."

Sterling was delighted. There were dozens of things he could do with that knife.

The big event of his birthday was the supper. Jack, Frank, and Ted arrived right on time. Faces and hands had been scrubbed as never before. Jack's shock of red hair had been brushed down until it looked like polished copper.

Grandfather Morton and Uncle Edward Morton were there, too. Sterling thanked his grandfather especially for his knife. It was just what he had wanted.

Uncle Edward, a great tease, said Sterling would soon cut off a finger or two. But Sterling declared he knew how to handle a knife as well as anyone.

Mrs. Morton knew just the kind of supper four hungry boys would like. There were generous servings of roast chicken and baked potatoes with large lumps of butter. There were dishes of dark red pickled beets, spiced peaches, and preserved pears.

A great plate was filled with hot rolls, fresh

from the oven, ready to melt thick spreads of butter. A pot of wild blackberry jam stood ready for the hot rolls. Sterling remembered the day they had gathered those berries. The sharp briars had scratched him, but he was rewarded by great handfuls of ripe berries. He ate quantities of them then, but he liked the jam, too.

Frank asked Jack if he had ever seen as fine a birthday supper in Connecticut.

"There could never be a better one than this," answered Jack. At that he heaped blackberry jam on his roll and popped it into his mouth.

At least that was his plan. But something happened to that jam! *Squish!* The jam swished from roll to freckled face.

Jack gasped. Sterling, Frank, and Ted stared. Then everyone roared with laughter. Jack's freckled face was spattered with dark red jam. It was like the make-up of a clown.

Of course Jack was embarrassed.

"Never mind," Mrs. Morton said with a laugh. "Never mind. Your stunt just added to the fun of the party."

Uncle Edward, who liked puns, said, "If you boys never get into a worse jam, you will be lucky." Then he added, "Don't let Sterling scrape off the jam with that new knife. He might cut your head off."

At last came the great cake. Eight small candles flashed their flames from the top. Sterling was thrilled as he blew out the candles with the biggest puff of his life. The other boys watched with happy looks on their faces.

Mrs. Morton then cut the cake with great care. Four great slices were placed before four eager boys. Everyone else was served generously, too.

The boys could scarcely wait until Mrs. Morton lifted her fork for the first bite. Sterling plunged his fork into the great wedge on his plate. The first bite was a big one.

Click!

A look of surprise came over his face.

His teeth had struck something hard. He was puzzled. The cake was more than cake. What might it be? What had happened?

His mother was smiling. "Don't try to chew everything which enters your mouth," she said.

Sterling explored his mouth and found a penny. It had been baked in the cake as a surprise. There it was—a shiny penny for good luck. In those days a penny was about the size of our half-dollar of today.

"Mine has one, too," shouted Frank. So it was for Ted and Jack.

"I think we are all lucky," said Frank.

Jack and Ted agreed. At that they went on to finish their portions of cake down to the last tiny crumb.

As the boys left the table, Mrs. Morton said, "I have one more surprise for you, Sterling. Your

Aunt Mary in New York has sent you something." At that she handed him a small package.

Sterling examined it for a moment. What might it be? Aunt Mary was his favorite aunt. He thought her red hair was very beautiful. Her merry laughter rang in his ears whenever he thought of her.

What had she sent?

Off went the wrappings. Inside was a neat little box. Sterling lifted the cover. "Dominoes," he shouted. "Just what I have been wanting."

In less time than it takes to tell it the boys were playing dominoes. It was the right game to end a happy frontier birthday.

When the playing was finished, Frank, Ted, and Jack thanked Mrs. Morton for the delicious supper. Then they wished Sterling many more happy birthdays as they left for their homes.

"Mother," said Sterling, "this has been the most wonderful day of my whole life."

Steamboats on Lake Erie

STERLING AND his pals liked boats. Is there a boy anywhere who doesn't?

The boys liked the little boats they made to float on puddles. Some of the boys had ridden in rowboats. But the most thrilling sight of all was to see the great steamboats on Lake Erie. When the long toot of the whistle was heard, Sterling would shout, "I will race anybody to the pier." Then off the boys dashed.

There was the long pier reaching far out into the lake. Sterling liked nothing better than to wander among the great piles of boxes, bales, and barrels.

"These goods have come from all over the world," he would say. "At last a lake steamer has left them right here on the pier at Monroe."

Sterling liked to show his friends how to tell what the goods were. A great box with strange characters meant China. Then by sniffing carefully, Sterling could detect the odor of tea.

"This is a shipment of tea from the other side of the world," Sterling explained.

Sterling led the boys on. "Ah! This is a barrel of vinegar."

It did not take much of a nose to find the boxes of codfish. Indeed some kind of fish smell seemed to cling to the pier almost all of the time.

The boys found their noses to be as useful as their eyes. The pier had more sights and smells than any place in town.

Sometimes a boy would cover his eyes. His pals would then lead him to a box or crate to guess by smell what was in it.

Sterling said, "A fellow can learn a lot through the nose."

They liked the smell of the bales of leather. It would soon be taken to the shop of the harness and saddle makers. There the boys would sniff the leather again and watch the saddle maker at his trade.

"The best time to go to the pier," explained Sterling is just before a steamboat arrives. Goods to be put aboard are on the pier. Passengers are waiting to go aboard. People come to meet expected relatives and friends."

Sterling had discovered a wonderful lookout. "Fellows," he said, "from the top of these piles, driven beside the pier, we can see far."

Sterling had learned just how to get to the top of the piles quickly and safely. Jack said he was glad there was room for several boys on that perch.

Once the boys were at the lookout, they would

strain their eyes for the first hint of an incoming steamer's arrival.

There it was! A thin wisp of smoke—or so it seemed—rising from the lake. The boys could see the smoke before they could see the boat. Now the smoke grew blacker, and the tall smokestack came into sight. At last the steamboat itself came into view.

Sterling would call out the names, "Superior," "Henry Clay," "Mayflower."

Each boy was eager to tell what he saw. All watched for the cloud of white vapor or steam. That meant the steamboat whistle.

When the boys saw that cloud of white, they would shout, "Thar she blows." Then silence. In a moment came the sound of the steamboat whistle—a wonderful long deep blast that was music to the ears of Sterling and his friends.

The boys often counted the seconds between seeing the steam and hearing the sound.

In that way they could tell how far away the steamboat might be.

Everyone on the pier watched eagerly. At the first sight the steamboat had looked so small.

"It is growing bigger by the minute," shouted Sterling excitedly.

There was another loud toot of the whistle as the steamboat drew near to the pier. How it startled the people, and how it amused the boys!

Then came the clanging of the bells, the snorting of the engines, and the shouts of officers and men. The great paddle wheels churned the water violently.

When the engines were still, lines were tossed. Great ropes or hawsers were made fast. The steamer had arrived.

Excitement was everywhere. People on deck waved to people on the pier who waved back and shouted.

When the vessel was snuggly tied fast, the gangplank was let down. As friends greeted friends, the crew and longshoremen rushed to unload the cargo.

Sterling and his friends were now on the pier. They were there to enjoy every bit of the arrival of a steamboat.

Sterling knew the names of many of the captains and often the names of other officers.

He listened to many stories told about the

early steamers. Some had been wrecked. Others had been stolen by bands of ruffians.

He would repeat each story to the other boys.

Sterling loved to tell the story he had heard about the "Caroline" which had been set on fire and cut loose near Niagara Falls.

He told it in a grand manner. With a flourish he would say, "I was told she drifted right down the rapids and over the falls, burning fiercely as she went."

"What a splash," exclaimed Frank.

None of the boys had seen Niagara Falls, but everyone knew about them. In their imagination they could see that great burning ship, as long as several houses, go smashing over the great falls.

Sterling was a natural story teller. These abilities were to serve him well in later years as a newspaper man.

The steamboat story that Sterling liked best

was the story about the first steamboat ever to sail on the Great Lakes.

There had been sailing ships on the Great Lakes for many years. But after Robert Fulton's successful experiment with his steamboat "Clermont" on the Hudson River, there was a rush to build steamers for the Great Lakes.

Sterling explained, "Sailing ships had been built at Black Rock, a place near Buffalo. Many of these ships had sailed right here on Lake Erie. Then came the first steamboat for the Great Lakes. It, too, was built at Black Rock."

"I suppose," said Frank, "that was done because the men at Black Rock knew how to build a good boat to run by sail or steam."

"That's right," said Sterling, "They were good boat builders."

"That first steamboat was pretty big," continued Sterling. "It was one hundred thirty-five feet long, with paddle wheels fifteen feet in diameter. Inside were the boiler and engine. The smokestack reached high above the deck.

"The strangest thing about it," said Sterling, "was the naming."

He continued the story. "A famous old chief of the Wyandotte Indians had been friendly to the white people. The whites decided to name the new steamboat for the old chief.

"His Wyandotte name was Mier. That was a short name, but it had a special meaning. To these Indians it meant a turtle—an animal that walks in the water."

"That," said Sterling, "was why the first steamboat on Lake Erie was named 'Walk-in-the-Water.' When it was launched, it took twenty yoke of oxen to pull it into the water."

The boys had listened wide-eyed.

"Well that was some boat, and what a name!" commented Ted.

" 'Walk-in-the-Water' was built to furnish

fine service between Buffalo and Detroit. Old piers were extended out to deeper water so that 'Walk-in-the-Water' would be safe when in port. They say that when that steamboat was finished, hundreds of people gathered to see it take to the water," said Sterling. "Very few people, whites or Indians, had ever seen a steamboat.

"Captain Job Fish came to be·captain of the new steamboat," explained Sterling. "He had been a captain on a Hudson River steamboat."

"I have heard that he was a great fellow," said Frank, "and it was a real honor to be captain of the first steamboat on Lake Erie."

"They say that hundreds of people came to each little port to see the new ship on its first trip," continued Sterling.

" 'Walk-in-the-Water' did not have a whistle. All of the steam was needed to turn the paddle wheels. In place of a whistle a cannon was put aboard. When near a port *bang* would go the cannon. Then everyone along the shore would rush to the pier.

"In some places the water near the shore was not deep enough for the 'Walk-in-the-Water' to land safely. People would then row out to the steamboat in small boats. Some went to meet passengers. Others went to receive cargo. Still others went just to see the new steamboat.

"Silly things were said about the new steamboat," Sterling went on. "Stupid questions were asked. Could it sail against the wind? What would happen if they had no fuel? Could the ship travel backward? For three years the 'Walk-in-the-Water' was a success."

"Why do you say for three years?" asked Frank. He knew Sterling would keep on telling the story if he knew the boys wanted to hear it.

Sterling excitedly told more of the story, "Well, a terrible gale came which swept the 'Walk-in-the-Water' ashore. The cannon was fired many times for help, but in the darkness of the night no help was at hand. *Crash* went dishes and furniture. Women shrieked, and children cried. At last 'Walk-in-the-Water' struck the lake shore and rolled on her side.

"The passengers were soaked and bruised, but no lives were lost. The engine was saved and used in two ships that were built later."

Sterling told this story as if he had actually been aboard the "Walk-in-the-Water" when it was swept ashore. It was a true story, but that ship was wrecked several years before Sterling Morton was born.

Monroe harbor was at the mouth of the Raisin River. Many puns and jokes were made over that name, *Raisin*. A riddle was "Are there currants (currents) in a raisin (Raisin River)?"

Sterling and his friends often explored the banks of the Raisin. Long before the white men came, the Indians had built a village at the site of Monroe. Indians could paddle their canoes down the river to the lake.

French settlers had come later. The Indian village became a French settlement called Frenchtown. The settlers had found the land to be very fertile. Soon they were growing crops and building good log houses.

The early French settlers had done one thing that pleased Sterling and his friends very much. They had planted orchards of pear trees. Sterling, the explorer, soon learned about these trees. He knew what they were and where they were. These pear trees were clustered along the banks of the Raisin.

Sterling said, "Some of those pear trees are fifty feet tall."

The boys liked best to explore that region when the pears were ripe. Sterling would say, "Tell all the fellows the pears are ripe."

Then off went the boys to feast on the pears.

After heavy rains the boys watched the water rise in creeks and rivers. The Raisin would become a great rolling current of muddy water rushing on to the lake. From the pier they could see the current of muddy water as it flowed far into Lake Erie.

Sterling never tired of watching the lake boats come and go. Most interesting of all were the passengers. He dreamed of the day when he might get aboard a lake steamboat. Perhaps he would travel to Buffalo. Maybe he would see the famous Erie Canal.

Such were the thoughts of Sterling Morton one day as he entered the Morton home. He was startled to find his father and mother talking very seriously. He thought his mother had been crying. What had happened? What did it mean?

Off to New York

JUST AS STERLING reached home and opened the door, he heard his mother say, "Shall I take Sterling with me?"

"What in the world can that mean?" thought Sterling eagerly.

His father and mother looked very serious.

This was strange. His mother seemed always to be ready to laugh. Sterling loved the twinkle in his mother's eyes. To him her laughter was like music.

Mrs. Morton wiped away her tears and put her arms around Sterling. For a moment she could not speak.

52

Then she whispered, "Sterling, we have just had word that your Aunt Mary is very ill in New York City."

"My Aunt Mary?" exclaimed Sterling.

To Sterling it could not be true. He could think of Aunt Mary only as a lively, laughing person.

"Yes," answered his mother, "and I feel that I must go to New York at once to help her."

So that was the reason for the question, "Shall I take Sterling?"

His mother went on to explain. "I have been talking with your father about going. It is a long way. I may be gone many weeks. I wonder if I should take you with me?"

"Oh, please do," pleaded Sterling. "I know I could be helpful. I shall be ever so careful not to disturb Aunt Mary."

His mother knew this, and she knew how fond he was of his Aunt Mary.

Sterling was sturdy and strong. He loved rough and tumble play with his pals as much as anybody, but he knew how to do the right thing at the right time. His mother was sure that she could depend upon him if he went with her to New York.

Sterling's thoughts were flashing through his mind. Like raindrops in a storm his thoughts were going helter-skelter. He thought, "I do want very much to travel on a lake steamer." He had heard many tales about New York. He did want to see that great city.

"Aunt Mary is my favorite aunt," he said aloud. "I would do anything for her."

Things had happened so fast that he could hardly think. What might such a trip really mean to him?

Sterling was very glad that his father and mother had considered before he came home that he should go to New York with his mother.

"When shall we start?" asked Sterling.

"Just as soon as possible," answered his mother. "Your father thinks the 'Fairport' is due to sail for Buffalo tomorrow."

"Oh, I know the 'Fairport'," said Sterling. "It is one of the biggest and best steamers on the lake. I have seen the captain, too,—Captain Jerry Brock. Men at the pier say he is about the best captain on Lake Erie. He has red whiskers and can shout his orders better than anybody else."

Sterling was growing more excited by the minute as they discussed the trip.

"How long will it take us to go all the way to New York? What things must we take with us?" came the questions.

Without waiting for answers Sterling said, "Just wait until I tell Jack, Frank, and Ted that I am going to New York." At that he dashed out of the house to tell the news to his friends.

He found his pals watching a mother robin feed her young.

"Come quickly, Sterling," shouted Jack. "Climb up here beside us and watch those robins in that big apple tree."

The boys were perched on planks to be used for a new building. From this point they could see four young robins with wide open mouths.

"What big mouths," exclaimed Sterling. "Those mouths look bigger than their heads."

"But that can't be," said Jack as the mother tucked another fat earthworm into one of the hungry mouths.

For a moment Sterling had been so interested in the robins that he almost forgot his news.

Then out tumbled the words. "I am going to New York. I am going tomorrow on the 'Fairport'." Sterling seemed to be bursting with the news. At such unheard of news the boys stared at Sterling. The robins were forgotten.

"I don't believe you," said Frank bluntly.

"Are you just fooling?" asked Jack.

"No, I am not," declared Sterling. "It is true."

He went on to explain. "Mother must go to New York to take care of my Aunt Mary who is terribly sick. She wants to take me with her. It is the most exciting thing that has ever happened to me. We leave on the 'Fairport' tomorrow afternoon."

At that he was off for home fairly bursting with excitement.

He found the whole family helping with the packing. Mrs. Morton explained, "We must take a trunk. We may be in New York for some time. We must take everything we may need."

This pleased Sterling. It meant that things now stored in the trunk must be taken out of it. To him that stout trunk was a treasure chest.

"Oh, what is that?" he asked. He pointed at a blue and white coverlet.

"That is a bed coverlet. Your Grandmother Sterling wove that herself on her own loom."

Mrs. Morton lifted out an old uniform.

"That uniform was worn by your great-grandfather, Captain William Sterling," said his mother. "He served in the Connecticut militia during the American Revolution."

"Did he really fight in battles?" asked Sterling.

"Yes, of course," came the answer, "with those old flintlock rifles and pistols."

Just then Sterling's father came in.

"Well, well," said Mr. Morton, "there is that old flintlock pistol."

"How did it work?" asked Sterling eagerly.

His father showed him.

Sterling listened and looked with wide open eyes. He could see just how it worked. Then with a sigh he said, "It was a slow way to shoot."

His father laughed and said, "Yes, but the flintlock was much better than bows and arrows."

After the trunk had been emptied, the packing was begun.

Sterling had never seen his things so neatly folded and tucked in. Besides clothing his mother put in jars of preserves and bags of dried fruit. These were foods Aunt Mary liked.

At last the trunk was full, and the top fastened. There was more packing the next morning. Sterling watched with more interest than ever. This time it was a huge lunch basket.

"Mother, do you think we will eat all this?" he asked. He had watched as rolls—the kind he liked best—a big cake, and a box of his favorite cookies were put in. "Of course, I could eat all of those myself, if given a little time."

There were also slices of ham, venison, boiled eggs, pickles, and preserves.

"We will not go hungry," exclaimed Sterling, "that's for sure." He rubbed his stomach at the thought of all the food.

His mother gave a little chuckle and closed the basket.

Soon the Mortons were at the pier. So were Frank, Jack, and Ted.

They and everyone in Monroe had heard the long toot of the whistle on the "Fairport."

"That toot was the very best I have ever heard," cried Sterling. "It really means something today. It means I am going to New York."

Sterling watched as the "Fairport" moved slowly to the pier. Captain Jerry Brock shouted orders. Great ropes were tossed to tie the vessel fast to the pier.

Jack, Frank, and Ted scrambled up to their lookout on the piles.

Sterling saw the men unload boxes, bales, and barrels of cargo. Then the out-going cargo was put aboard.

Sterling's father led the way as Sterling and his mother walked up the gangplank.

60

"Captain Brock," said Mr. Morton, "this is my wife and my son Sterling."

"I am glad to have them aboard," replied the Captain. "I am sure we can make them comfortable on their trip."

Then looking sharply at Sterling, he said, "My boy, I will show you all over the ship. We will see the engines, anchors, and all the rest."

"Oh, thank you," answered Sterling.

What boy wouldn't like an invitation such as that one offered by Captain Brock?

As the "Fairport" pushed away from the pier, Sterling waved from the deck to his pals on the cluster of piles as long as he could see them.

Captain Jerry Brock kept his word and took Sterling to all parts of the ship.

Sterling liked the engine room best. There he watched the great piston chug back and forth and heard the steam sizzle and sputter.

It was thrilling to stand on the bridge and

watch the turning of the pilot wheel to guide the ship. Sterling had watched from the pier many times, but to be right there in the pilot house was wonderful.

"Captain Brock," said Sterling, "I have wanted to travel on the 'Fairport' more than to do anything else. Thank you so much."

"You are welcome, my boy," Captain Brock replied graciously. "I hope you and your mother have a wonderful trip."

Sterling watched from the deck to be one of the first to see Buffalo, New York.

"I think I see it," he shouted.

"Buffalo sighted," called a ship's officer.

"You see," explained Sterling to his mother, "we boys have learned how to look across the water. We look for boats. Now I look for the town in the same way."

There was a great hustle and bustle at Buffalo.

People pushed their way into the crowd on

the pier. Bells clanged. Engines huffed and puffed. Men shouted. Passengers gathered along the railing.

Crewmen tossed the great ropes to tie the "Fairport" fast. Down came the gangplank.

The Mortons were in Buffalo at last.

"Hack, lady?" shouted a driver to Mrs. Morton. She nodded her head to the man with the carriage and horse for hire.

Sterling and his mother climbed into the hack. Off they went as the horse's hoofs clop-clopped their way to the Erie Canal.

The canal boat was waiting.

Sterling found it all very exciting as he and his mother transferred to a canal boat.

"Now we are on the great Erie Canal," observed Sterling. "The canal boat is not like the lake ships at all."

The canal boat was smaller and very flat.

Sterling quickly explored it.

He heard no sizzling steam. There was no chugging engine. No paddle wheels churned the water.

Horses would pull the canal boat along the quiet waters.

No waves dashed the shore as on Lake Erie.

Sterling said, "It is much like a raft. It is like the one I saw at home on the Raisin River."

"Cut away," shouted the captain.

On the bank horses, hitched to the end of a long rope, pulled hard. The canal boat moved very slowly at first.

"We are moving, Mother!" exclaimed Sterling. "It is a hard pull for the horses at first, but it will soon be easier."

The driver cracked his whip, and the horses were soon at a slow trot.

"Low bridge," called the Captain.

Everyone seated on the deck ducked low as the canal boat passed under a bridge.

"This is fun," remarked Sterling, "but I like the big ships we have on Lake Erie much better."

At last Mrs. Morton and Sterling reached Albany, New York.

Here they would go aboard a fine Hudson River boat, "The Lady Richmond."

Sterling was amazed as they came to the Albany pier.

There were more people waiting than he had even seen at a pier. Men wore tall top hats. Ladies were richly dressed. They were bound for the great city of New York.

Nothing escaped Sterling's sharp eyes.

He felt the difference between the Michigan frontier and the settled life of New York State.

Sterling watched closely. "Mother, this boat is much finer than the 'Fairport'. See how big the decks are!"

Sterling enjoyed the excitement of people rushing about just before sailing time.

66

He and his mother were startled at the great long blast of the whistle.

"That whistle is a big one, too," said Sterling with a laugh. "I nearly jumped out of my skin."

Then came the *chug, chug* of the engine and the splash of the paddle wheels.

The "Lady Richmond" took to the middle of the great Hudson River.

Sterling knew that the river was named for Henry Hudson the explorer.

"Mother," asked Sterling, "when did Henry Hudson discover this river?"

"Over two hundred years ago," came the prompt reply.

How different it was from the lake where the "Fairport" kept far from the shore.

Now on the great "Lady Richmond" endless scenes seemed to float past.

"Something new comes along every minute," exclaimed Sterling.

Sterling's mother kept calling his attention to the scenes along the way.

The great Hudson River grew wider and wider. Sterling could see farms and villages along the beautiful high banks.

"This is really a giant river," exclaimed Sterling. "It is fifty times as big as the Raisin."

Now Sterling could see New York City. How exciting everything was.

"New York is more than a hundred times as big as Monroe." he gasped. "Maybe a thousand times as big."

"Just see all those great ships," he fairly shouted. "There are all kinds! And see the different flags."

"Each country has its own national flag," his mother explained, "and ships come to New York from all over the world."

Slowly their steamer moved up to the pier.

Sterling watched every movement. He saw

the lines thrown to shoremen. Then the great ropes tightened.

"We are here. We are in New York," he shouted. "If only Jack, Frank, and Ted could see this! What a lot of things I shall have to tell them."

To Sterling it seemed that hundreds of people went ashore.

At last it was the turn of the Mortons to leave the "Lady Richmond."

"How will we go to Aunt Mary's home?" asked Sterling. In those days there were no telephones. The telegraph had not yet been invented.

"Your Uncle Fred has no way of knowing we are here," explained his mother. "We shall take a hack. I have the address."

Sterling watched the hack driver put the trunk in the rack. Then the driver helped Mrs. Morton to her seat. Sterling hopped into his place as Mrs. Morton told the driver where to go.

Bumpity-bump went the hack, and *clinkity-clink* the iron horseshoes on the cobble stones.

Sterling had never before seen a paved street.

He was excited over everything he saw. He did not know a city could be so big.

Then his thought turned to his Aunt Mary.

Sterling was very serious as he said, "Mother, I do hope Aunt Mary is better. I like her so much, and she is such fun."

Frontier Boy in New York City

STERLING WATCHED eagerly from the hack as it clattered along a street lined with red brick stores and houses.

Houses, houses everywhere!

How different from Monroe!

Where were the trees and open spaces?

Where did the children play?

Sterling and his mother chatted about the ways of the great city.

"I think we are nearly there," she commented.

"This is it, lady," called out the driver as he reined in his horses.

Uncle Fred must have been watching.

The front door popped open, and Uncle Fred hurried down the steps.

"I am so glad you have come. Mary keeps saying she wants so much to see you," said Uncle Fred. Turning to Sterling, he said, "She talks as much about you, Sterling, as about your dear mother."

"Will I be allowed to see her and talk to her?" asked Sterling.

"Yes," answered his uncle, "for only a few minutes at a time. She is very ill."

Sterling was shocked when he went quietly into his aunt's room. She was so weak and so very pale.

But a smile brightened her face as she held out her hand and whispered, "Sterling."

Sterling was almost in tears as he said, "I wanted so much to come, Aunt Mary, and mother said I could."

During the next few days Sterling explored his

72

aunt's house. How different it was from houses in Monroe. Sterling looked at every part of the house, inside and out. He wanted to know all about it.

The houses in New York were crowded together. Sterling wondered if they were trying to push each other out of the way.

He walked up and down the street.

There was a number on each house. They did not have numbers on the houses in Monroe.

Sterling was glad to find a tiny garden at the back of his aunt's house. He liked the pleasant back porch with steps leading down to the little garden.

Best of all was a hammock reaching from one corner of the porch to another. Sterling stretched out in the hammock and looked at the ceiling. How comfortable and lazy he felt.

Suddenly Sterling made a discovery. He looked carefully again to be certain.

Sure enough up in the corner of the porch was a robin busily building her nest. "So you are a city robin, I suppose," said Sterling to himself.

In a few minutes Sterling was off to tell his mother and Uncle Fred. "I have found a robin building a nest on the back porch. Come and see it, please."

Sterling, pointing to the nest, said, "I just wish Aunt Mary could see it. She loves birds."

When the doctors came the next day, they thought it best to cut Aunt Mary's long hair. She was so weak that it tired her to have her hair combed.

Sterling thought Aunt Mary's red hair was the most beautiful hair he had ever seen. He watched as a nurse cut the long strands of hair and put them in a box. He also saw the box placed on a shelf.

Suddenly Sterling thought of something, but he told no one about it.

74

Soon Aunt Mary began to grow stronger. People no longer spoke in whispers.

Aunt Mary now enjoyed taking food.

Uncle Fred could go to his office each morning.

Sterling was allowed more time with his aunt.

One day someone asked what had happened to Aunt Mary's hair after it had been cut. No one seemed sure about it. Where was it?

Perhaps Sterling knew.

"Oh, yes," answered Sterling. "I gave it to the robins. I knew Aunt Mary loved robins. They have woven that red hair into their nest. It is beautiful. Come and see."

When Sterling went home a few weeks later, one of his treasures was the robins' nest showing beautiful strands of red hair. When the young robins had left the nest, Uncle Fred had given the nest with the red hair to Sterling.

"How long are we going to stay in New York, Mother?" asked Sterling.

Mrs. Morton replied, "Your Aunt Mary is much better, but I must stay with her until she is well and strong. She has been very ill."

Each morning Sterling went in to see his aunt.

Aunt Mary said, "You are the best medicine I get, Sterling. You always cheer me."

Sterling laughed and asked, "Am I a kind of pill for you each morning?"

Sterling settled down to learn about the great city. He was allowed to explore streets near Aunt Mary's home.

The big thrills came when he could go with Uncle Fred to other parts of the city.

As he went about the city, Sterling wished that his pals of Monroe could be with him. He did miss his old friends.

One morning Sterling met a boy who lived in a house near his Aunt Mary's.

"Good morning," said the boy. "I am Ralph Bates. What's your name?"

"I am Sterling Morton from Monroe, Michigan. I came with my mother who is taking care of my aunt who has been very sick." Sterling greeted the boy heartily.

Sterling was glad to find a friendly boy in the big city.

"I am not allowed to go far from my home, but I can show you some places," suggested Ralph.

"I am not allowed to go far either," agreed Sterling, "but now that my aunt is better, my Uncle Fred has promised to take me about the city when he has time."

The boys started down the street.

"What do I smell?" asked Sterling, sniffing and looking about.

Ralph laughed. "You smell the fish market. I want you to see it. Let's go in and watch them clean the fish."

Sterling had never in his whole life seen so many fish.

Ralph explained, "This big fellow is a sword-fish. See that long snout that looks like a sword? He is a fighter until he is caught but very good eating when cleaned, dressed, and cooked."

Sterling looked into a great tank of wriggling eels. Nearby he saw a large bin of dark green crawling creatures.

"Are these lobsters?" asked Sterling.

Ralph said that they were.

"They look like the crayfish we catch along the banks of the Raisin," said Sterling, "only these are fifty times as big. Why are those little pieces of wood stuck in those big claws?"

"That," said Ralph, "prevents the lobsters from tearing each other apart."

Sterling watched the lobsters. "Are they really good to eat?" he asked.

"Oh, yes," said Ralph, "they are very tasty. When they are boiled, they turn from green to a beautiful red."

"And what are these?" asked Sterling.

"Oysters," answered Ralph. "Come back here and see how they shuck oysters."

Sterling watched a woman "shuck" the oysters. With a blunt knife she pried open the shell, quickly turned the knife, and out dropped the oyster. "Want to try it?" she asked. It did look easy to do.

Sterling took an oyster and the knife. Try as he might, he could not open the oyster.

Sterling sighed, "I just can't do it, and for you it looks so simple."

The woman laughed and said, "Tricks in all trades." At that she flipped out another oyster.

Sterling was fascinated by the many fish.

"Where do they all come from," he asked.

"Oh, we are right near the ocean," answered Ralph. "Fishing is a big business here."

Sterling had become so interested that he had forgotten about the smells of the fish market.

"What a story I can tell my pals in Monroe," he said as he and Ralph walked home.

Sterling was delighted to have made friends with Ralph. There were so many things Sterling wanted to see in New York, and Ralph was happy to share his knowledge with Sterling.

Sterling was pleased, too, when his Uncle Fred took him about the city.

One day they went to the southern tip of Manhatten Island. "This is where New York City began," explained his uncle.

Sterling looked out upon the great New York harbor. "I have never seen so many ships," he said. "They are going and coming all the time. Do they ever bump each other?"

"Sometimes they crash, especially in a heavy fog," Uncle Fred admitted.

"Is that really the mouth of the Hudson River?" asked Sterling. It was so wide that it looked like a part of the sea itself.

"It is," Uncle Fred answered. "The great Henry Hudson sailed his Dutch ship 'Half-Moon' right past this point and up the Hudson River. The Dutch built a fort here. Later came the English."

Sterling thought it a perfect place for a fort.

As they turned away, Uncle Fred asked, "Sterling, would you like to ride on a streetcar."

"Oh, yes," answered Sterling. "I have seen them on the streets, but I have not had a ride."

Sterling and his uncle climbed aboard.

Two horses were hitched to the car. The driver stood at the front to guide the horses.

Clang! Clang! went the gong. The horses pushed hard against the harness, and the street-car moved along the street.

Sterling was impressed by the large city.

"That hotel is larger than a dozen such as we have in Monroe," he said. "The stores are so big, too."

When they reached Aunt Mary's, Sterling told his mother and aunt of the wonderful things he had seen.

Then Sterling added, "Uncle Fred is going to take me to a big political parade, too."

On the night of the great parade Sterling was very much excited.

"I have heard people talk and talk about politics and parades," he said. "Now I shall see what happens." Sterling, like most of us, did love a parade.

As Sterling and his uncle walked along the streets, boys and men kept shouting, "Tippecanoe and Tyler, too!"

"What does that mean, Uncle Fred?" asked Sterling.

His uncle laughed and said, "It is a part of election excitement."

"I know about election excitement," said Sterling. "My Uncle Edward Morton publishes

The Monroe Advocate. He is always excited about elections."

"I like the sound of 'Tippecanoe and Tyler, too,' but what does it mean?" asked Sterling.

"Tippecanoe is a creek out in Indiana," began Uncle Fred.

"General William Harrison was a great Indian fighter. The Shawnee Indians decided to defy and fight the white people of Indiana. Chief Tecumseh was their great leader.

"When Tecumseh stirred up the Indians, General Harrison went into action. He led a fighting army of white men against the Indians.

"The Indians were driven out, and their village was burned. It was a great victory for General Harrison.

"This happened near Tippecanoe. General Harrison had become a hero. Ever since people have called him Old Tippecanoe.

"Now," continued Uncle Fred, "Harrison is a

candidate for president of the United States and Tyler for vice-president. 'Tippecanoe and Tyler, too' is a wonderful slogan. The people love it, and they love the old Indian fighter. They sing it. They shout it. They put it on banners."

"They do love Old Tippecanoe," agreed Sterling enthusiastically.

Sterling and his uncle pushed their way through the crowd. People were singing and shouting.

Uncle Fred found a good place to stand.

"If we stand right here, Sterling, we can see the parade and watch the crowd."

Such crowds! Such a noise!

Then came the sounds of marching bands.

Sterling could hear the *boom, boom, boom* of the big bass drum. The trumpets blared.

Far down the street Sterling could see men carrying flags and banners. Many people carried flaming torches.

The noise from the parade and the crowd grew louder and louder. The parade was coming nearer.

Even more exciting were balls of fire or fiery stars popping in the air. They were shot from pasteboard tubes called Roman candles.

Now Sterling could see streams of sparks flowing from the Roman candles. Out would come a fiery star, then more sparks, and still more stars in many colors.

Thousands of colored stars were shot into the air as the parade marched, marched along.

First in the parade was a great banner—"Tippecanoe and Tyler, Too." The crowd shouted it over and over, and Sterling joined in.

"Oh, what is that?" asked Sterling excitedly. "It looks like a log cabin on wheels."

"It is," answered Uncle Fred. "Harrison was born in a log cabin. This is to show how a poor boy may become great in the United States."

86

"I like that idea," said Sterling.

His uncle went on to say that Harrison's opponent, Martin Van Buren, was a rich man. Harrison was not rich. The people who were for Harrison wanted to show how the men were different so they chose the log cabin.

"Van Buren is now president and wants to be elected again. The Harrison people want to turn him out of office," explained Uncle Fred.

"See what is coming now, Sterling," suggested his uncle. "Look at that banner and see what it says. That banner means that these people do not want Van Buren as president. They often call him Old Van."

Sterling saw the banner and read:

> "Farewell, dear Van
> You're not our man
> To guide the ship
> We'll try old Tip."

"We sometimes say the President of the

United States is the Captain of the Ship of State," explained Uncle Fred. "These people think if Old Tippecanoe could battle the Indians he will be a good president."

"Now I understand," said Sterling. "The way this crowd is shouting I think Old Tippecanoe is going to win."

At last Sterling and his Uncle Fred started home. The crowds scattered.

"Uncle Fred," said Sterling, "This is the most exciting time I have ever seen. I do thank you for taking me."

Sterling trudged off to bed. He was tired but happy. He had felt the excitement of a great city and a presidential campaign.

Now he was dreaming of the things he would tell Jack, Frank, and Ted when he went back to Monroe, Michigan.

School Days

STERLING MORTON was off to school.

It was a beautiful morning in early autumn. Colorful leaves from the maple trees fluttered to the ground. Sterling liked to walk among the trees now that he was back in Monroe.

Sterling felt good that morning. He liked the bright sunshine. He was glad to be on his way to school.

He knew that he could learn much at school. He liked books, and he liked to study.

He also liked to learn by roaming through the woods and about the town. But that was a different kind of learning. He liked both kinds.

Sterling heard much talk about books and reading at home. His Grandfather Morton was a printer who knew a lot about words and how to spell them.

His Uncle Edward Morton published a newspaper—*The Monroe Advocate.*

Sterling liked to visit the newspaper office.

Just now he was thinking of school and of seeing his friend Jack Bradford. On that morning Sterling planned to stop at Jack's home. Then the boys would be on their way together.

"Hi!" shouted Jack as he stood in front of the Bradford home.

"Come on to school, and put your head to work," answered Sterling.

The two boys started down the street. As they trudged along, other boys joined them.

"I say, have you fellows seen the crop of nuts this year?" asked Sterling. "The walnut and hickory trees are loaded."

"Oh, I have seen them," answered Frank, "We can gather them by the bushel this year."

"Just wait until Jack Frost comes around," Sterling reminded the boys. "He will really knock them down. Then we must all go nutting."

"To go nutting" meant that a group of children would gather nuts.

Jack Frost was their best helper. When a hard frost came, the ground under the walnut and hickory trees would be covered with nuts.

Just now there was warm sunshine. Jack Frost would be around later.

At the moment Sterling and his friends must continue on their way to school.

The school was built of logs and rough lumber. It was very different from our schools.

"This is a nice schoolyard," said Sterling as the boys neared the school.

"We surely have had some good games here," added Ted.

The boys had reached the door of the school. Schoolmaster Whipple was watching.

"Scrape the mud from your boots," ordered Mr. Whipple.

A long flat piece of iron had been fastened to the edge of the platform outside the door. Each pupil must scrape the mud from his shoes before he entered the building.

As Sterling scraped his boots, he muttered, "Some day I hope we have walks wherever we go in Monroe."

At that time there were sidewalks on only a few streets in Monroe. It was still a frontier town without many conveniences.

As the boys went inside, they hung their caps on wooden pegs near the door. Holes had been bored in a log, and round pegs had been driven into the holes.

"The worst thing about this room," remarked Sterling, "is that it is so dark."

The room was lighted by four small windows. On a day of bright sunshine these served well enough. In winter the place was often dark.

At one end of the room was a huge fireplace. A box of firewood stood near it. The older boys took turns in placing logs on the fire when the weather was cold.

At the other end of the room stood the teacher's desk. It was placed on a small platform. From this point the teacher could see the whole school without leaving his chair.

Sterling said that Mr. Whipple, sitting up there, looked like a king on his throne. He said this to his pals, not to Mr. Whipple.

"He has a collection of scepters, too," added Sterling.

"What do you mean—scepters?" asked Jack.

"Well, it is like this," said Sterling. "When you see the picture of a king, he is seated on his throne and is holding a scepter in his hand."

"Yes, I have seen pictures like that," answered Jack quickly.

"That scepter—that fancy little stick—shows his authority to rule," explained Sterling. "Now Mr. Whipple has that bunch of switches right within his reach to show who rules the school."

Frank added, "And if a pupil breaks a rule of the school, whack will come the scepter from King Whipple."

The boys laughed, but they knew that Frank was right.

The pupils sat on crude benches made by sawing a log in two. Auger holes had been bored in the round side of the log. Then strong peg legs were driven in the holes. The flat side of the log had been smoothed to sit on. There were no backs on the seats to lean against.

A shelf-like desk had been built along the walls. The older pupils, who could write, did their work there.

Not a wall map nor a picture was to be seen in that school. There was no blackboard.

Sterling urged his pals to do good work in school, too.

"I mean to be somebody," insisted Sterling, "and I know I must do my school work. A fellow with an empty head is not worth much."

Frank, Ted, and Jack always listened when Sterling talked like that.

"The fellow who can read and write well," Sterling explained, "is going to be the important man in business.

Mr. Whipple was very strict. He demanded that the children study quietly.

If a pupil's writing was not the best he could do, Mr. Whipple made him do it again.

The pupils in that school were of different ages. At that time schools were not in grades as they are today.

Some pupils were just learning to read. Other pupils could read very well.

Sterling was already a good reader, but he did not write very well. He tried hard to improve his writing.

Mr. Whipple watched Sterling as he formed each letter. If it were not his very best, Sterling Morton received a rap on his knuckles.

Almost all of the schoolwork in that Monroe school was reading, writing, and arithmetic.

People called them the three R's.

There were few books in Sterling's school. There were few books in any frontier school in those days, not even many textbooks.

Of course there was no library.

Sterling spent much time studying from his "blue-backed" speller. That speller was famous in the pioneer schools.

Noah Webster was the author. The title was *American Spelling Book*. This same Noah Webster later was the author of the famous Webster's Dictionary.

This "blue-backed" speller was more than just a spelling book. It was also like a reader.

Sterling knew that if he could learn to read this book well he might learn much from other books and newspapers.

He found many good suggestions in that book.

Sterling's father, a stern and religious man, thought the suggestions very good.

Here are some of the things Sterling found in Noah Webster's Spelling book:

"A good child will not lie, swear, or steal. He will be good at home, and ask to read his book.

"When he gets up, he will wash his face and hands clean.

"He will comb his hair and make haste to school.

"He will not play by the way as bad boys do.

"Never pester little boys."

Sterling learned these things well, but he did not always practice them.

Sterling enjoyed his work in arithmetic.

Sterling used *Pike's Arithmetic* in school. Some of the rules in *Pike's Arithmetic* were more difficult to understand than a practical problem.

"What is the difference between six dozen dozen and half a dozen dozen?" Sterling read aloud to his friends.

"That is a tricky one," said Frank. "Read it slowly, and let me think about it."

Sterling read it again.

"This is the tricky part," explained Sterling. "Half a dozen dozen is the same as six dozen. The extra word *dozen* is the rascal. The answer is 792."

"Oh, I see the point now," exclaimed Jack.

"Here, fellows, is the crazy one," said Sterling with a chuckle. "Just listen to this." He read: "If 8 boarders drink a barrel of cider in 12 days, how long would it last if four more came among them?"

"A barrel of cider is a lot of cider," put in Jack.

"Oh, it is just a foolish book problem," said Frank. "Let's be off."

"All right, let's go, but the answer to the cider problem is eight days. I'll show you how to get it someday."

Sterling did not worry about his studies. He could do any school work he tried. He soon became a very good reader.

Whenever he read a book or a paper, Sterling would plan to tell his friends what he had read.

Nothing pleased Sterling more than to gather his friends about him and tell them what he had been reading. This was a great help to his friends who cared little for reading. At least it helped them to get along in school. It meant much to Sterling because he read with great care so that he could tell the story well. He would keep in mind important points.

Sterling was getting much education outside the school. He learned many useful lessons as he watched from the pier, saw houses being built, and stopped to see the blacksmith at work.

He was also a good listener. He liked nothing better than to stand by as men talked.

The men often talked politics. He liked what they had to say about the future of Monroe and Michigan. He would grow up and be a part of it.

Sterling liked best the tales told by soldiers and earlier settlers. Tales about battles with the Indians were really thrilling.

But now Sterling was in school. He had said he was going to be somebody. He knew he must do well in school if he were to succeed.

To hold the attention of his listeners Sterling would make his point exciting. He would gesture with his hands. Sometimes he might shout a part and then speak in a whisper.

Sterling Morton, while still a schoolboy, was getting practice as a public speaker. He hoped someday to make political speeches.

He wanted to become a political leader.

He said to his friends, "Some day I shall write reports for newspapers that will really make people pay attention."

After school had been dismissed for the day, Sterling liked nothing better than to talk to his young friends.

The boys talked about school as they walked on down the street. Both Sterling and Jack liked to read.

"One of the best places for me to read," said Sterling, "is in the office of my Uncle Edward. He is the editor of *The Monroe Advocate*."

"That must be a good place to get news," said Jack enviously.

"It surely is," answered Sterling, "All kinds of papers are sent to that office. Men meet there to talk, too. I like to listen to them."

"It is a wonderful place to learn things."

"Let's go visit *The Monroe Advocate* right now," suggested Sterling.

At that Sterling and Jack were on their way to explore Edward Morton's Print Shop.

Uncle Edward's Print Shop

STERLING AND Jack Bradford entered the office of *The Monroe Advocate.*

It was a frontier newspaper office.

The editor's office was at the front of the building. Edward Morton's desk was covered with papers and scribbled notes.

Through an open door at the back Jack could see the printing press and cases of type.

"Hello, Uncle Edward," called out Sterling in a cheery voice.

His uncle looked up from his desk and put down his pen.

As Edward Morton came forward, Sterling

said, "This is my friend, Jack Bradford. You met him last spring at my birthday party."

"Howdy, Jack," said Uncle Edward as he shook hands with both boys.

Sterling wondered how soon his uncle would make a sharp remark. His uncle had always teased him.

Sterling like his uncle and tried to get even on the teasing if possible. Just now Sterling was uncertain. With his pals he was always the leader, but now he seemed timid.

Sterling watched his uncle as he looked sharply at both boys.

"I am glad to meet you, Jack," said Edward Morton, "but you are not very particular about choosing your friends."

That was just like Uncle Edward, thought Sterling.

He knew that his uncle was only teasing, but he must answer back.

"Well," said Sterling, "he has just now slipped down another notch by coming in here."

His uncle laughed. Then said, "I am glad you fellows came in."

Turning to Jack, he said, "I tease this young fellow a lot, but I am always glad to meet his friends."

Edward Morton and the two boys chatted for a few minutes.

The boys told about their school work and some of their trips into the woods.

Turning to Sterling, Mr. Morton said, "Show Jack around the place, and then I shall put both of you to work."

Sterling let the way to the print shop. It was a large room at the back of the building.

"Can you smell the printer's ink?" asked Sterling eagerly.

Jack sniffed and answered, "I surely smell something different."

"Some people say that once a fellow smells printer's ink and likes it, he will be a newspaper man," said Sterling.

The boys wandered about the shop.

Although it was Jack's first visit, Sterling had been there many times and knew much about it.

The two boys stopped to see a man busily setting type.

Sterling explained the plan.

"You see there are two cases. In the upper case are the capital letters. In the lower case are the small letters."

Jack looked carefully at the type cases.

"Why are there so many little boxes in each case?" Jack asked.

"Each letter has its own box," explained Sterling. "There is a box for *a*'s, another one for *b*'s, and so on."

Sterling laughed. "We use more of some letters than others," said he. "Think how many more times we see the letter *e* than the letter *x*. That means the *e's* must have more room."

Sterling had watched Grandfather Morton set type many times.

With the help of his grandfather he had set the type for his name—Sterling Morton.

"Suppose," said Sterling, "we want to set the type for your name,—J—a—c—k. First we take the capital letter J from the upper case. Upper-case means capital. Then we take the other letters from the lower case. Lower-case letters mean small letters."

The boys watched the typesetter as he worked. He wore a great leather apron to keep the printer's ink from soiling his clothes.

"Each one of these little pieces of metal is a letter," said Sterling. "That metal tray or box in the typesetter's left hand is a composing stick. He picks up each letter with his right hand and places it in the composing stick in his left hand."

Jack sighed, "What a lot of work. Each letter must be placed just right so we can have something to read."

The boys watched the nimble fingers of the typesetter. There was a little click as each letter was put in place.

Click, click, click went the type, as they were placed in the composing stick.

"Now this is the printing press," explained Sterling. "The type is locked in an iron frame, or form, the same size as a page of the newspaper. Printer's ink is put on the type with a roller—something like your mother's rolling pin. Watch how the men do it."

The two boys stood watching. The ink was rolled on the type. Then the white paper was spread on the type. Down came the press as a man pulled hard on a great lever. One side of the paper was printed. The other side would be printed from another frame of type.

"Here are the fresh *Monroe Advocates* just off the press," one of the men told the boys.

Sterling's Uncle Edward was looking over a copy with great care. Edward Morton did not like to find a printing mistake in *The Monroe Advocate*.

Turning to Sterling and Jack, he said, "All right, you fellows can help now by folding papers. This is the way to do it."

Edward Morton folded two or three papers to show the boys how to do it.

Sterling and Jack went to work with a will. This was one step in becoming a newspaper man that was easily learned. Sterling did want to be a newspaper man some day.

At that time the printing of a newspaper in a small town was done by hand work. The type was set by hand because there were no type-setting machines.

The printing press was operated by hand, too.

It took a strong man to work the press. It was hard slow work, but it was very important.

Sterling's Grandfather Morton had spent much of his life as a printer. Now he and his son Edward were publishing *The Monroe Advocate*.

Sterling Morton learned many things in the office of *The Monroe Advocate*. He liked to hear his Uncle Edward talk with important men.

The people of Monroe called Edward Morton a "hot-head." Perhaps he was. He did write lively stories about Monroe and Michigan.

The Monroe Advocate always praised Monroe and Michigan. Uncle Edward was a booster for the home town. Some people said he was a real boaster.

Sterling liked this spirit.

He would sit quietly and listen as his Uncle Edward and political leaders talked and talked. Then he would tell his friends what he had heard the men say.

"You should have heard what I heard at *The Monroe Advocate* office," Sterling told the boys. "Mayor Barton and Major Dodge were talking, and several other men came in. They talked a lot about new inventions."

"I should like to hear that," exclaimed Jack.

"They keep talking about the steam engine and how it is being improved—especially the locomotive," continued Sterling. "Those men are determined to have a railroad built right here in Michigan."

"There are more and more miles of railroad being built, and of course more locomotives and cars," added Ted.

"Have you fellows ever heard of a revolver?" asked Sterling.

"I have heard of it," said Frank, "but I do not know how it works. I know it is a kind of pistol."

"That is right," said Sterling. "Those men also talked and talked about that. They think it is a

112

great thing for settlers going west if they must fight the Indians."

"But how does it work?" asked Ted.

Sterling explained, "It is a pistol with a cylinder that holds five or six shots. The cylinder turns or revolves. That gives it the name re-volver. With six shots it is equal to six old pistols of one shot each."

"Cowboys and scouts are using it out west as they ride horseback over the plains." suggested Frank.

"The Major said it is a wonderful invention for the army," said Sterling. "He said it was in-vented by Samuel Colt in Connecticut."

"Oh, I have heard about that," said Jack, "be-fore we left Connecticut."

"Sometimes Judge Lawrence comes into the office," said Sterling. "Then the talk is about rail-roads. But the men talk of two kinds of railroads. One is the real railroad they want to build here.

The other is the underground railroad. Do you fellows know what the underground railroad is?"

"I do," said Frank, "It is not a railroad at all. It is a plan to help Negro slaves escape to Canada to be free."

"We all know that in the South we have slave states," commented Ted.

"Many Negroes are kept as slaves down there," Jack added. "Naturally they try to run away—to escape."

"What do your uncle and the judge have to say about the underground railroad?" asked Ted encouraging Sterling to talk.

"I was surprised," said Sterling, "when they said there were slaves in Detroit. Almost all, if not all, have been set free. Detroit is now a very important station on the underground railroad. Let me explain," Sterling added as he settled down to tell a long story.

His pals made themselves comfortable and

114

ready to listen for they liked to have Sterling tell them the things he knew.

"The underground railroad is not a railroad at all. It is a lot of farm houses where the families will hide a runaway Negro slave. Each farm is called a station. There are some stations in towns, but almost all are in the country."

"Are there any here, or near here?"

"We do not know," answered Sterling. "None of the men at Uncle Edward's office knows for sure. Everyone knows that these slaves head for Detroit. Once in Detroit they soon slip across to Canada. Then they are safe and free.

"Judge Lawrence says he is afraid we may have a war over these slaves some day. He says he does not want any slave cases in his court."

"The underground railroad certainly sounds dangerous. Sterling, you are lucky to hear grownups talking about such exciting things," Ted spoke enviously.

The boys had enjoyed hearing the news stories, and Sterling had had a wonderful time telling them.

After pausing for a moment, Sterling asked, "Do you know the most wonderful story of all?"

Frank, Ted, and Jack pricked up their ears.

Sterling continued, "It is not about guns. It is not about the hard life of slaves. It is not about underground railroads."

It seemed Sterling would never stop.

Frank was impatient. "For heaven's sake what is the big story, Sterling? You keep saying it is not this, that, or something else. We want to hear what it is."

"We surely do," chimed in Jack and Ted.

Sterling chuckled. He loved to excite his pals about events in Monroe.

"Well, now, just be patient," he began. "This is a story about a railroad, but it is not underground. In fact this railroad is not anywhere."

"What do you mean—a railroad that is not anywhere?" asked Jack impatiently.

"Is is a ghost railroad or a dream railroad?" asked Ted.

"That is exactly what it is. It is still a dream. Those men at the office dream and talk about it by the hour. Some of these days," said Sterling, "that dream will some true right here in Monroe.

"We shall build a railroad—not underground —but on a grade. It will not be for runaway slaves. It will be for the Judge, the Mayor— maybe for the Governor—really for all of us."

"You don't mean it," exclaimed the boys.

"Yes, I do," answered Sterling. "It is a dream now, but some fine morning the people will wake up and find the dream has come true.

"Remember, my pals! A big story is coming— a railroad story!"

Coming of the Railroad

"THE GRADERS have started," shouted Sterling.

Frank leaned on his spade and blinked his eyes. Ted dropped another fishworm into a can and straightened up. Frank and Ted had been busy digging fishworms.

"What do you mean, the graders have started?" demanded Frank.

"The graders for the new railroad," exclaimed Sterling, almost bursting with excitement.

"How do you know the graders have started?" asked Ted.

"Well, you know I have been telling you about the railroad that everyone wants," Sterling an-

118

nounced proudly. "There has been more talk about that railroad at the office of *The Monroe Advocate* than anything else.

"Judge Lawrence got so excited about it that he stood on a chair and yelled, 'Hurrah for Monroe!' You should have seen him.

"My Uncle Edward was almost as wild. He told how he would spread the news on the front page of the paper. Then he started on what the headlines should be."

GREATEST EVENT IN MICHIGAN
MONROE—FIRST IN EVERYTHING
STEAMBOATS! NOW STEAM TRAINS!
SPEED AND LUXURY BY TRAIN

"Most of the prominent men in town came in," continued Sterling. "They have been talking about the railroad for months. Now the work has begun."

"It takes a long time to build a railroad," Frank reminded him.

"They are just now starting to build the grade for it. But those men imagine all kinds of wonderful things.

"But let's go take a look. I am all excited about it. Let's pick up Jack."

Frank and Ted stopped digging fishworms.

"The fish will just have to wait for their tasty worms," said Ted.

Off went the three boys.

They went to the Bradford home to tell Jack.

"They have started to build the grade for the new railroad. We are on our way to see how they do it," called Sterling.

Jack joined the other three boys.

The four boys hurried on to the site of the future railroad. There were the graders!

Never before had Sterling and his pals seen so many men, horses, and mules at work.

The boys knew about the plan to build the railroad from Monroe to Petersburg.

120

Everyone had been talking about it for many months.

The boys had watched the surveyors at work.

A surveyor is a man who takes measurements and writes descriptions of land and water. From his work the best place for building a street or railroad is chosen. It is very important that the work be done with great care.

To have the best place for a railroad the one who draws the plans must imagine how it will be when finished.

A surveyor's work will show where it will be necessory to move dirt, cut down trees, build bridges, and even make a tunnel through a great mountain.

The plan for the railroad was much like the plan for a street only it must be made with greater care.

"You see," said Sterling, "the grade for this railroad must be level."

Now the boys watched the graders at their difficult work.

There was excitement everywhere.

Hundreds of men were at work.

No tractor, bulldozers, or motor truck had been dreamed of at that time. Men, mules, and horses did all the work.

Drivers shouted at their horses.

Mule drivers cracked their whips and shouted even louder.

"They say a mule is the slowest and laziest animal we have," cried Sterling over the noise.

"Because mules are slow and lazy," shouted Frank, "mule drivers are sometimes called mule skinners. When the drivers uses his whip, the mule's hide is so thick he does not feel the lash very much."

"The horses are different," said Sterling. "They are more sensitive. Just a word of encouragement will make them do their best."

"There are surely some fine big horses here," remarked Jack. "They look strong enough to pull anything."

"This place is like a beehive," commented Sterling, "only here the bees are men, mules, and horses."

Six great horses were hitched to a big plow.

"See how that plow tears up the sod," shouted Sterling. "They loosen the sod with a plow so the scraper can scoop up the dirt and take it to the grade."

Scores of men and boys stood about, watching the workers.

Sterling and his friends were out to see everything. They pushed their way through the crowds. They climbed trees to get a better view. Sometimes they almost got in the way of the workmen.

"How those horses sweat in pulling the slip-scrapers," exclaimed Sterling.

"Yes, and the men who hold the slip-scrapers are sweating, too," said Jack. "The men are working as hard as the horses."

The slip-scraper, at that time, was the best tool for building a railroad grade. It was the best that railroad builders had for many years. The slip-scraper was made of sheet iron. It was like a huge shovel with handles at the side.

First the earth was loosened by a plow. Then a team of horses pulled the scraper through the loose earth.

On the under side of the slip-scraper were two smooth iron runners. These runners were the slip part of the scraper. It slipped along on those smooth, flat iron runners.

It was hard work to hold the scraper in position as it was being filled with earth. The horses could pull it, but the men must hold it in place.

It took a strong man to hold a slip-scraper.

"Do you see how it works?" shouted Sterling.

"They scoop up the earth at the side and then dump it on the grade," exclaimed Jack.

"In that way there is a drainage ditch on each side," said Frank.

"How do they know how high to build the grade?" asked Jack.

"That is where the surveyor comes in," answered Sterling. "After final plans were made from his studies, stakes were set to show how high the top should be."

"There are other stakes to show how wide the grade should be," said Ted.

With a laugh Sterling said, "This is why the surveyor's studies are important in making plans, and the graders do the work."

Then Sterling added, "And the surveyor gets the best pay because he has a good head and understands mathematics."

"They really have one kind of train running here now," said Ted. "I mean the trains of scrapers with a team of horses hitched to each one. Each is filled with earth, pulled up, and dumped on the grade."

The boys watched the steady movement of the line of horses, scrapers, and men.

First, was the struggle to fill the scraper.

Then the horses pulled it along on the runners to the grade. At just the right place the load of earth was dumped on the grade.

Round and round they went, filling, pulling, dumping, and going back for more earth.

"Look over there," exclaimed Sterling, pointing to a group of well dressed men.

"There is Judge Lawrence out to see the graders at work. I heard him say the railroad can not be built too soon," Sterling added. "You should hear the Judge, Uncle Edward, and some of the others talk about this railroad."

The boys came day after day to see the graders at work.

At last the first part of the grade was finished.

Even with a large crew at work it took much labor and time to do the job.

"Those slip-scrapers and teams of horses are wonderful," said Sterling, "but after they have done their best, the grade must be made smooth by men with shovels."

"Yes," said Frank, "there are nearly fifty men working with shovels right over there."

At last the earth in the railroad grade was in its proper place.

Sterling and his friends stood looking at the level surface. "Isn't it a beauty?" cried Sterling.

"It is finer than any street in Monroe."

As the boys watched, along came another gang of men. Great wagons drawn by four-horse teams were loaded with short logs. Now the men began placing the logs across the grade.

"What are they doing with those logs?" asked Jack.

128

"Oh, I know about them," said Sterling, "I heard the men talking at Uncle Edward's office. Those short logs are called ties. The rails are spiked to them. The rails in that way are tied fast. That is why the logs are called ties."

Then the long wooden rails were placed on the ties.

"How carefully they measure everything," remarked Ted.

"They must," said Sterling. "If a rail were out of line half an inch, it might wreck a train."

After the wooden rails were in place, another crew and more great wagons brought long narrow iron plates.

"Now what are those things?" asked Jack.

Sterling explained, "Those are iron plates to be nailed on top of the rails. The wheels of the locomotive and the cars will roll on those smooth iron plates. If the iron plates were not there, the wood would be worn out in no time."

Neither the boys nor the builders knew that in a few years rails would be made entirely of iron or steel.

The graders were now far away from Monroe. They were building the grade all the way to Petersburg.

The railroad began to look like a real railroad.

The ties, the rails, and the iron plates were being rapidly put in place.

"Let's not come back until next Saturday," said Sterling. "Then we can really see a great change."

Early next Saturday morning the boys were up and ready to be on their way. It seemed they could not travel fast enough. What had happened since they were last there?

"Ah! What a sight," yelled Sterling. "Come up here, you fellows, and look. The railroad is finished as far as we can see."

Everyone looked carefully.

QUIZ BOWL
SCHEDULE

**Beginning:
Monday, Feb. 2**

Mondays: 3:40-4:30
(Fifth Grade Only)
Tuesdays: 3:40-4:30
(Sixth Grade Only)

Wednesdays: 7:30-8:05
Thursdays: 7:30-8:05
3:40-4:30

**Quiz bowlers must attend at
least 2 practices a week in
order to compete.**

Upcoming Competitions:
February 24: 6th MATH Contest   April 15: 5th MATH Contest
April 27 & 28: National Thinking Cap Quiz Bowl

Sterling was right as usual.

The boys were just turning away.

"Wait a minute," cried Sterling.

There was something unusual in Sterling's voice. All stopped to listen.

"Fellows, I have the biggest news yet," announced Sterling. He waited a moment with a strange smile on his face.

"Well, let's have the news," said Frank a little impatiently.

"The news is this. The first locomotive ever to reach Monroe will be on the 'Michigan' when she arrives at the pier next week."

His pals shouted and tossed their caps into the air.

"Who will be there when she arrives?"

"Everybody," was the shouted reply.

A great event was not far away.

The First Train

STERLING HAD been watching his grandfather set type for *The Monroe Advocate.*

There was a steady *click-click* as each letter slipped into the right place.

As he watched his grandfather, Sterling overheard voices in the office of his Uncle Edward.

He could hear the deep voice of Judge Lawrence speaking loudly.

Now he heard the clear, sharp comments of Lawyer Mann. There were also other voices.

The men seemed to be growing excited. What might it be?

Sterling heard the word "locomotive."

132

That was the cause of the excitement.

Sterling slipped into a good listening spot.

The Judge was saying, "That railroad they built from Toledo, Ohio, to Adrian, Michigan, three years ago is really not a railroad."

Sterling listened.

"The cars on that railroad are pulled by horses," said Judge Lawrence. "What kind of a railroad is that?"

"Well," said Lawyer Mann, "I suppose that is a railroad, but without a steam locomotive it does not amount to much."

"Well, if the 'Michigan' makes port in Monroe this afternoon," said Edward Morton, "we shall have a locomotive for our railroad.

"So that is what all the loud talk is about," said Sterling to himself.

As Sterling listened, the men grew more and more excited.

So did he.

The new locomotive was aboard the "Michigan," one of the best steamboats on Lake Erie.

It was due today—this very afternoon.

At the thought of it Sterling slipped out of the office and dashed down the street.

He ran as if rushing to a fire.

What a story he had to tell those boys!

Sterling found Ted, Jack,and Frank lounging under a spreading apple tree.

At the moment those fellows were anything but excited.

Jack turned to Sterling and said slowly, "Does anyone have any news about the railroad?"

Jack spoke as if he were half asleep.

Sterling knew he had the news that would really wake those boys from their day dreams.

"I wish you fellows could have heard what I have just heard at the *Advocate* office," he boasted. "Do you know what is happening this very afternoon, here in Monroe?"

Sterling was bursting with enthusiasm.

"Every fellow in that office was excited. Judge Lawrence says this is the biggest event that ever happened in Monroe."

Jack, Ted, and Frank stared.

"The locomotive is coming on the 'Michigan' this very afternoon," exclaimed Sterling.

The boys jumped to their feet.

"Tell us some more about it," said Jack.

"Those men said that locomotive is the biggest thing ever put aboard the 'Michigan.' It weighs tons and tons."

"Why do they call it the locomotive instead of just the engine?" asked Ted.

"Oh, that's easy," said Sterling. "I have talked about that with my father and Uncle Edward. A locomotive is an engine that can move itself on rails. Some steam engines stand still.

Then Sterling added, "Of course many people call a locomotive an engine."

All four boys relaxed and settled down again under the apple tree.

Sterling had brought thrilling news.

They had been talking about that locomotive for weeks.

Suddenly Sterling popped up like a jack-in-the-box.

"Listen, you fellows," he demanded. "Listen!"

There was not a whisper.

"It is the whistle of the 'Michigan'," he shouted. "Old Captain Blake knows how to pull that whistle cord."

Now the long toot of the whistle was clear.

Every boy was on his feet.

"Let's go," shouted Sterling. "Everybody in town will be at that pier very soon.

The boys raced to the pier and scrambled up to their lookout.

Far out on the lake black smoke poured from the smokestack.

Now the "Michigan" itself could be seen.

As Sterling and his pals watched, there came a great cloud of white vapor.

It was the longest, deepest blast the boys had ever heard.

Captain Blake intended for everyone to know that the "Michigan" was making port.

Again and again came the long deep sounds of the whistle.

By the time the "Michigan" moved slowly up the pier, hundreds of people were on hand to see the unloading.

The biggest derrick in the harbor was in place.

"Just look at those big ropes," said Ted.

"They are specials for this unloading," explained Sterling. "They have placed the locomotive at the middle so it would not tip over the boat."

The men fastened the great ropes.

Would they be strong enough?

Could the derrick really lift it?

As the ropes and pulleys began to creak, Sterling shouted, "Watch her now. They are lifting her."

Slowly the boiler swung clear of the deck.

Men guided it toward the pier.

Then came the wheels, smokestack, and other parts. Even before the "Michigan" sailed, men were at work to put the parts of the locomotive in place.

Sterling and his friends watched.

The new locomotive had really arrived.

It would soon be ready to go chugging down the newly laid railroad tracks.

Soon the great day, too, had arrived.

Posters had announced it. *The Monroe Advocate* had a big story about it.

Wherever Sterling went, people talked about the first train. Flags were flying. Shops and stores were decorated.

138

Crowds were beginning to gather.

A speaker's stand had been built near the railroad station.

Sterling had explained the plans to Ted, Jack, and Frank.

"There is to be a big parade," he had said. "It will start at the court house. Colonel Brown will be the Chief Marshal. He will be handsome on that black horse of his. The Governor is coming and will make a speech. The band will play, and soldiers will march."

The boys were at the court house to see the parade form in line.

Colonel Brown was wearing his finest uniform. He was ready to start the parade.

Then all was quiet.

"Forward! March!" shouted Colonel Brown.

The trumpets blared, and the Governor's carriage moved forward. Sterling and his friends marched in step with the band.

There was a great crowd at the station.

Everyone was dressed in his best.

Many listened to the music and the speeches.

Sterling and his friends went at once to see the train. They were more interested in the sizzling steam of the first locomotive in Monroe than in hearing the speeches.

As soon as the speeches were over, the train would move down the new railroad.

Sterling led the way along the train.

He pointed to the firewood piled high on a car next to the engine. "This locomotive is a wood-burner," he said. "We have more wood than coal in this part of Michigan."

The engineer stood beside the train waiting until the progrem was finished.

"Sir," asked Sterling, "would you explain to us just how the steam turns the wheels?"

"Of course I will," came the reply.

"The steam flows into this cylinder," said the

engineer, "and drives the piston to the other end. Then the steam enters that end to drive it back. The piston is fastened to the bar on the drive wheels. As the piston goes forward and back, the drive wheels turn and move the train."

"Just think," said Sterling, "there is the first locomotive in this part of Michigan."

"Yes," commented Jack, "and we are right here to see how it works."

The boys looked at every part of the train.

"See how the wheels fit the rails," said Sterling. "It is a good thing those strips of flat iron are on the wooden rails. Without them the wood would be worn out in no time."

Suddenly the boys heard a round of applause.

"The speeches are finished," shouted Sterling.

"Now the real event begins!" yelled Ted.

The people who had listened to the speech by the Governor moved nearer to the train.

The band played lively music.

People shouted and cheered.

Sterling and his friends were on hand to see every movement.

"There is the Governor wearing his high hat," said Frank.

"And there is his wife," said Jack. "Isn't she beautifully dressed?"

The important people were on their way to board the first train in Monroe.

Sterling talked about the fine carriages.

Today we talk about railroad cars. We say sleeping car, dining car, flat car, and so on. During the first few years of the railroads in the United States it was different. People then talked of railroad carriages.

Those first carriages were much like horse drawn carriages. They were longer and had more seats for passengers.

All this interested the people as they gathered about the train.

Sterling, as usual, explained important points to the other boys. He had heard so much talk about it at the office of *The Monroe Advocate*.

"Each carriage has seats for twelve people," explained Sterling. "There are several carriages in each train."

Now the boys were looking at the nicely covered seats.

"Those seats are as nice as parlor chairs," said Frank.

"They should be for the people who will sit on them today," laughed Sterling.

The ladies, dressed in fine clothes, were being helped aboard.

Gentlemen, wearing long-tailed coats and tall hats, found their places.

Soon all passengers were aboard.

People beside the train waved, cheered, and shouted to their friends.

Some tossed flowers to the passengers.

Flags and red, white, and blue bunting decorated each carriage.

"See how the people are protected from rain and sun," explained Sterling.

He pointed to the carriage top.

Some of the very first railroad carriages were made without tops.

"Those curtains at the side can be drawn when it rains or if it is cold weather."

Sterling and his friends were right beside the locomotive when the last passenger climbed aboard the train.

The fire roared in the firebox under the boiler.

Smoke poured from the smokestack.

Steam sizzled and hissed.

"This iron horse is really ready to go," said Sterling eagerly.

"All aboard!" came the call.

The bell began to clang.

There was a long *toot-toot-toot*.

146

The engineer moved the throttle.

The steam rushed to move the pistons.

The pistons moved the bars to the drive wheels.

With the hissing of the steam, the shouts of the crowd, and the toot of the whistle the first train in Monroe moved slowly down the track.

Early Teens

STERLING HAD passed his twelfth birthday.

He was growing up.

His mother laughingly said he ate more food than anyone else in the family.

No boy in Monroe was more active than Sterling Morton.

Strong and large for his age, he roamed about the town. He was eager to see everything that happened.

If a crowd began to gather, Sterling would soon be there. Should a fire break out, he would make a dash to see it.

If there were an accident, Sterling would be

on hand. If there should be a fight, he wanted to know about it.

He not only was eager to see these happenings but also wanted to tell about them.

Even as a boy he was a natural reporter of events. In future years as a newspaper man he would report great events.

"What a chicken fight that was," exclaimed Sterling.

He and Jack were on their way to meet Ted and Frank.

"Hi! you fellows," shouted Sterling. "You should have seen the chicken fight I saw last night," said Sterling.

Nearly every family in frontier Monroe kept a small flock of chickens. This was a good way to be sure of a supply of fresh eggs.

Sterling liked fresh eggs, but he liked even better to see chickens fight each other.

Roosters have been famous fighters for centuries. If Sterling and his pals saw a rooster sneaking into a neighbor's flock, they watched for a fight.

Some times the boys encouraged the roosters to fight. Once a rooster had crossed to another yard, the fight would be on. Sterling loved it.

Cockfighting or chicken fighting is an old but cruel sport. People on the frontier were used to cruel Indian fighting. To many of these rugged settlers chicken fights seemed mild.

Sterling's father, a stern religious man, did not approve of the chicken fights that were held in Monroe. He did not want his son to have anything to do with them.

Sterling, however, soon learned where the chicken fights were held. By one excuse or another he would go to see them.

He delighted his friends by telling them of the bloody battles but never a mention of them to his father.

"Tell us about the chicken fight," insisted Frank and Ted.

"I am glad my father can not hear this tale," admitted Sterling. "The more I grow up the closer he watches me."

"Maybe he thinks you are getting too wild," said Jack.

"I think that is it," answered Sterling.

"But I must tell you about that chicken fight.

"This chicken fighting is also a kind of French and Irish fighting. You know there are a lot of Irish settlers near Sandy Creek. The French are up the Raisin River.

"Pierre Leval is French, and Mike O'Kelley is Irish. They hold these chicken fights in that old warehouse near the pier.

"That last fight was a hot one.

"Pierre brought a new rooster called Napoleon, a very handsome fellow.

"Mike appeared with Pat.

"For weeks they have been training these roosters to fight. They feed them well. They toss them into the air to make them flutter and kick for exercise. That makes them strong and active.

"The roosters weighed the same. They were ready to go.

"Mike had Pat tucked under his arm. Pierre held Napoleon.

"As the men brought those birds together, those roosters stiffened for battle.

"Napoleon snatched some of Pat's feathers and Pat struck at Napoleon's eye. Those birds were really ready to fight.

"Over a hundred people were there.

" 'Pit your birds,' said the referee.

"Pierre and Mike placed the roosters on the dirt floor.

"Bing! Those roosters were at each other like flashes of lightning. They leaped. They fluttered. They crouched, and they pecked.

"Now they were in the air. Now they were on the ground.

"The men had fastened sharp steel spurs to the roosters' legs. The spurs worked like tiny daggers stabbing brutally.

"In no time Napoleon was bleeding badly.

"Another round and Pat had lost an eye."

Sterling stopped for a moment.

153

"It was a terribly bloody fight."

"How did it end?" asked Jack.

"Both roosters collapsed," said Sterling. "The French thought Napoleon had won. The Irish believed Pat was the winner.

"Such excitement!" said Sterling. "My father doesn't approve of chicken fighting, but I just want to see everything that happens."

Frank, Ted, and Jack had been impressed by the story of the chicken fight.

The boys liked Sterling very much, but they also knew that he had a strict father. They began to wonder what might happen to Sterling for going to the chicken fight.

Not long after this incident something important did happen to Sterling.

J. D. Morton, Sterling's father, was eager for his son to do well. Mr. Morton knew that Sterling was bright, that he liked school, and that he loved to read.

154

When Mr. Morton heard of some of his son's pranks, he decided to take action. He decided that Sterling should attend Wesleyan Seminary at Albion, a village about a hundred miles away.

Wesleyan Seminary was a Methodist boarding school.

The rules were very strict.

Sterling's father was a loyal Methodist. He feared his son was getting too wild and that he needed discipline.

Mr. Morton read the strict rules of Wesleyan Seminary. He believed they would be good for Sterling to practice.

All students were to rise at the ringing of the bell. Then they were to sweep and adjust their own rooms.

Mr. Morton thought that a good exercise for any boy in his teens.

All students must attend chapel for prayers, morning and evening.

Students were not allowed to run, jump, whistle, or yell in the halls.

They must not make loud noises on Sunday.

They must not use tobacco. They must not use profane language.

Mr. Morton made the arrangements and then told Sterling of the plan.

Sterling decided to report to his pals at once.

"Well, what is the big news?" asked Frank.

Sterling chuckled. "It is not about chicken fights," said he. "The simple fact is that my father prefers that I attend school rather than chicken fights. I know the plan is a good one. I just do not like to give up my prowling around here in Monroe."

Sterling looked thoughtful.

"You fellows know that I want a good education. This is my chance. I am to attend Wesleyan Seminary at Albion," Sterling announced very sadly.

There was a downcast look on each face.

The four boys had become close friends.

Now their leader was about to leave Monroe.

"I am sure it is for the best," admitted Sterling, "but there is a touch of punishment about it. My father wants to stop me from doing things I should not do. Now I shall be in a good school away from my old haunts."

The four boys sat and talked for a long time. There was a good supply of apples.

They tried to think of the future.

"One thing I know," sighed Sterling. "I shall not have better friends than you."

"You are right," said Frank, "but I wonder what pranks you will try at Wesleyan Seminary when you get to Albion?"

"So do I," admitted Sterling with a sly grin on his face. "Anyway I will leave for Albion on the Friday morning train."

To Boarding School

STERLING HAD accepted the plan for him to attend Wesleyan Seminary. He knew he was entering a new kind of world.

He would miss racing to the pier to climb to the lookout.

His friends would miss his stories. Sterling would miss telling the stories.

More than anything else he would miss *The Monroe Advocate*. At Albion there would be no Uncle Edward to tease him.

Sterling did a lot of thinking just before leaving for Wesleyan Seminary.

He knew he would miss Frank, Ted, and Jack.

In some ways he would miss the boys as much as his family.

Friday morning came with a burst of warm sunshine. It was autumn. It was the time for schools to begin. The nights were beginning to grow cool, even chilly.

Sturdy Sterling was eager and full of energy.

He would study hard, and he would also make new friends.

Sterling and his parents had gone early to the station. Frank, Ted, and Jack came soon after.

Those boys might be late to school some time, but they would not be late today.

They walked up and down the platform and took a good look at the locomotive.

Clang, clang went the bell.

The conductor called, "All aboard."

Sterling said good-by to everyone, climbed the steps, found his seat, and looked out the window.

The engineer grasped the throttle.

Slowly the steam sizzled against the piston.

The Friday morning train was on its way to Albion. Sterling was on his way to Wesleyan Seminary at last.

This was Sterling's first real ride on a train.

He looked out the window. Trees, fences, and houses seemed to flash by.

He heard the steady *clickety-click, clickety-click* of the wheels on the rails.

His thoughts were rushing along, too.

"My thoughts are going lickety-split and the wheels go *clickety-click*," he said to himself.

In a few hours the hundred miles had rolled by. There was a long blast from the whistle.

"Albion! Albion!" called out the conductor.

The train moved slowly to a complete stop.

Mr. Morton had arranged for Mr. Clements, a young minister, to meet Sterling at the train.

Mr. Clements shook hands and said he was glad to see Sterling.

It was a friendly meeting.

Sterling was now a strong, healthy youth eager to learn.

He would learn not only from books but also from the many activities of the Seminary.

"Here, Happy," called Mr. Clement. The driver of a hack hurried up to the platform.

"This is Sterling Morton, a new student," explained Mr. Clement. "Sterling, this is Happy Dillon. He is really Michael Dillon, but everybody calls him Happy because he is always very happy."

"That I am," replied Happy, "with all the nice people of the likes of you and a lot of others."

He spoke in a delightful Irish brogue. A broad smile spread over his face.

Sterling was pleased with Happy's warmth and good humor.

He was reminded of his Irish friends in his hometown, Monroe.

"And what can I do for ye, Mr. Clement and Master Sterling?" asked Happy.

"We should like to be taken to the Seminary," said Mr. Clement.

"Yes, and I also have a small trunk," added Sterling courteously.

"I shall load the trunk and take ye at once," came Happy's answer.

"Tuck yourselves in, and off we go."

"Come on, Hickory," called Happy to his horse. The hack rattled along the way.

"Why do you call your horse Hickory?" asked Sterling to be friendly.

"My lad," answered Happy, "that horse is as tough as a hickory stick, so I call him Hickory. He pulls this hack around all day and likes it, and I like him as I do a friend."

All this pleased Sterling.

Mr. Clement was pleasant, too. He was cordial, young, and lively.

162

Sterling was glad to be in Wesleyan Seminary where he would spend the next four years.

Soon Sterling was off to explore the grounds. He must learn all about the place.

Quickly he would know as much about Albion as he knew about Monroe.

Of course he missed his old friends.

"If they were here, what a time we could have," said Sterling to himself.

But Jack, Ted, and Frank were a hundred miles away. He must make new friends. He must be a real member of the school.

It was a determined Sterling who now went striding across the grounds.

How friendly those great trees seemed!

He often said that trees, next to people, were his best friends.

Sterling loved trees. As he strode along under the trees, they seemed to mean more to him than ever before.

He looked up at the colorful red and yellow leaves of the maples, oaks, and elms.

The trees made him feel at home. He was among friends because he was surrounded by trees he knew.

As he turned toward the river, a lad about his own age walked briskly toward him.

"I am Glenn Brooks," the boy said as he extended his hand. "Are you a new boy?"

"Right you are," came the answer. "I am Sterling Morton from Monroe. Where do you usually live?"

"Oh, I live in Detroit," answered Glenn. "Fred Storey and I came here together. I am a second year boy. I am glad to meet you. Let's walk and talk together."

That suited Sterling.

"We have strict rules in this school, but it is a good place to be," commented Glenn. "We have a lot of fun, too."

164

The two boys were now near the river.

"This is the Kalamazoo River, isn't it?" asked Sterling of his new friend.

"Yes," answered Glenn, "and it is a famous old river."

"It is surely a funny name," remarked Sterling.

"The students make up all kinds of crazy rhymes about it," said Glenn, "such as,"—

> Kalamazoo, Kalamazoo,
> How do you do, and how do you do.
> Kalamazoo, Kalamazoo,
> The Profs will give you a lot to do.

Sterling laughed. "I like those rhymes," he said. "I may try making some of my own."

"Good for you," said Glenn. "I hope you do. You must meet Fred Storey. His uncle is a big newspaper man in Detroit."

At the words "newspaper man," Sterling listened carefully.

When Sterling and Glenn entered the building, there came a cheery, "Hi, Glenn."

Sterling saw a smiling face, a shock of red hair, and a sprinkle of freckles across a turned-up nose.

"This is my friend, Fred," said Glenn, "and this is Sterling Morton, my new friend."

The three boys climbed the stairs to their own private rooms.

Classes would begin in the morning.

Sterling slept soundly that first night.

As he slowly roused himself the next morning, there came a great *ding-dong* from the tower bell. His room was almost under the tower.

"What a banging by a big bell," exclaimed Sterling as he bounced out of bed.

He remembered the rule to sweep and adjust his room and then go to chapel.

He dressed quickly, put his room in order, and went to the morning prayers.

166

There was a strict rule that all students must attend chapel morning and evening.

The Principal of the Seminary read from the Bible and offered the prayers.

Students joined in singing hymns.

Sterling did well in his studies, especially in English.

He loved to read and talk about what he had read. If there were an argument, Sterling Morton wanted to have a part in it. He soon became a leader among the students.

In this school there were literary societies. They were organized by the students themselves. Each member took his turn in making speeches, joining in a debate, or reading a paper.

Sterling soon became president of a society called "The Clever Fellows." This was just to his liking.

He had had good practice in reading things to tell to Jack, Ted, and Frank.

There were even more books and magazines here at the Seminary than in the office of *The Monroe Advocate*. He spent hours and hours reading them.

He was now learning to write interesting stories. He wrote about more people coming to Michigan. Sometimes he would write humorous rhymes. He was always ready to debate.

Sterling was always ready for a prank or a joke. Glenn told Sterling that he was "full of too much mischief."

"Perhaps you are right," came the reply. "You, Fred Storey, and the others must help me get over it."

Wesleyan Seminary was a boarding school. It has been said that the food at a boarding school never pleases everyone. Students often complain about the food even when the food is very good.

Sterling thought the limit had been reached

when very strong or rancid butter was served. Students in all parts of the dining room were sniffing and making faces.

"This butter is strong enough to walk," whispered Glenn. Only those near heard him.

"This stuff," said Fred, "is not only strong enough to walk, but it is strong enough to run. It may run us out of the dining room."

Several students giggled.

A fat boy bluntly said, "It stinks."

170

Sterling said nothing.

As he listened to the remarks, he planned a prank to do.

The next morning there was great excitement in Wesleyan Seminary.

The doors in the upper hall had been smeared with the rancid butter.

What a mess and what a smell!

Suspicion quickly pointed to Sterling Morton.

A special meeting of the faculty was held. Who had played this prank?

Sterling was called before the faculty.

"Did you do this?" demanded the Principal.

"Yes, sir," came the frank reply.

"Can you tell us why you did such a thing?"

"Yes, sir, I can. I heard so many students talking about how strong the butter was that I tried an experiment. I wanted to see if it were strong enough to pull the handles off the doors."

After the "bad butter" incident the faculty

kept an eye on Sterling. But the students were pleased that no more strong butter was served that year.

Sterling's four years at the Seminary raced by.

Near the end of his course he stopped to think of what they had meant to him.

He had studied hard and liked it.

He had played pranks and had fun.

What now?

He would go to the University of Michigan.

Most important to Sterling at Wesleyan Seminary had been the presence of Caroline French.

To Sterling she was the loveliest girl in the whole world.

They would not forget each other.

West to the Prairies

STERLING MORTON was ready for college. He was more determined than ever to be somebody.

Still eager to be a newspaper man, he knew he must have a good education.

He hoped to get into politics.

Sterling was a strong, tall, handsome fellow. He seemed never to grow tired. He read and studied for hours. He liked pranks, jokes, and arguments. A more energetic young man would have been hard to find.

Sterling had decided the best college for him was the University of Michigan at Ann Arbor. In 1850 he enrolled for four years of study there.

At that time the University of Michigan was not the huge institution that it is today. There were fewer than 100 students.

Sterling plunged into college life.

As at Wesleyan Seminary he soon became a leader. He debated, talked politics, and wrote news reports.

Sterling's roommate's name was Elihu Pond from Coldwater.

"What a combination of names," said Sterling with a laugh. "You are a wonderful fellow, but Pond from Coldwater must be Icy Pond to me. I christen you with that nickname."

Sterling joined Phi Phi Alpha literary society which met each Friday evening. Rare was the meeting in which he did not take part.

It was Sterling Morton who started the first student publication at Michigan. He gave it the high sounding title of *The Peninsular Quarterly and University Magazine*.

174

After four years at the university Sterling Morton became a newspaper man.

He was now on his way as a reporter for the *Detroit Free Press.*

Wilber F. Storey was the editor.

Sterling found Storey as firm and determined as his Uncle Edward. He made sharp and cutting remarks, but he was a friend to the young reporter.

Sterling loved Michigan, but he had a real longing for the great prairies of the west.

His thoughts were on Nebraska.

"How can you turn to Nebraska?" asked his old friend Judge Lawrence. "You say that, next to people, trees are your best friends. Nebraska is the most treeless territory in the whole country. It is not at all like Michigan."

"That may be true," answered Sterling, "but the soil is rich. I shall show the people how to grow trees."

It was October 30, 1854.

The train for Chicago moved slowly out of the Detroit station.

That very day Caroline French had become the bride of Sterling Morton. They were on their way to the Nebraska prairies.

A large company of their friends had gathered about the train to say and wave good-by.

"I think this is the most wonderful day of our lives," said Caroline.

"I think so, too," answered Sterling, "but there are even greater days ahead for us."

Sterling and Caroline looked out the window upon the changing scene along the way.

"Just see those flame red sumacs," said Caroline. "There are bright colors everywhere."

Rabbits hopped away, and squirrels scrambled up the trees. Horses were frightened by the roar of the train, the shriek of the whistle, and the clouds of smoke.

176

"Chicago! Chicago!" called the conductor.

The train was slowing down.

Sterling and Caroline looked out at the network of railroad tracks.

"What a tangle of railroad tracks," exclaimed Caroline.

The next day the Mortons were off for Saint Louis, Missouri. The train passed through a rich farming region.

From the train they looked out on great fields of corn.

"This is the best corn-growing land in the world," declared Sterling.

Suddenly there was a wonderful view of the Mississippi River.

The train neared Alton, Illinois, a town built high on the bluffs overlooking the great Mississippi River.

"Just look," cried Caroline. "What a mighty river it is."

"The greatest river in North America," declared Sterling, "and it drains those wonderful fertile prairie valleys."

The Mortons were soon in Saint Louis.

Sterling and Caroline walked along the waterfront. Steamboats were tied up all along the Saint Louis docks of the great Mississippi.

Some boats carried cargoes south to New Orleans and beyond. Other boats were on their

way north. Some boats would follow the Mississippi as far as Minneapolis and Saint Paul.

Sterling and Caroline Morton waited for a steamboat to take them up the Missouri River.

"The Missouri or 'Big Muddy' cuts right across the state of Missouri," explained Sterling. "At Kansas City it becomes the border between Missouri and Kansas. It is the whole eastern border line for Nebraska."

The Mortons were ready to board the "New Lucy," the steamboat that would take them farther on their way to Nebraska.

Dock workers loosened the great ropes that tied the "New Lucy" to the wharf.

There was a long blast of the whistle.

"This is surely a 'Big Muddy' river," said Caroline, watching the slowly turning paddle wheels.

"The sad part is that the good soil from the fields of our Nebraska is on its way to the Gulf of Mexico," answered Sterling.

When they reached Saint Joseph, Missouri, a new problem arose. The water was too low in the Missouri for the "New Lucy" to go farther.

What could the Mortons do now?

As soon as the "New Lucy" docked, Sterling was out to find a way to go on to Nebraska.

He soon learned that a stage line ran from Saint Joseph, Missouri, to Saint Marys, Iowa.

Saint Marys was just across the Missouri river from Bellevue, Nebraska, where the Mortons wished to go.

"It is the River Valley Coach Line," Sterling was told. "It is a good line with good coaches, good horses, and good drivers."

Sterling hurried back to the hotel to tell Caroline he had booked passage to Saint Marys.

"We start tomorrow morning at six o'clock," said Sterling, "The stage coach will pick us up."

"That is an early hour to be up and away," said Caroline with a laugh.

180

"So it is," answered Sterling, "but I know we can do it."

"All aboard for the northbound stage coach" came the roaring call of Proprietor Gibson at six the next morning.

Sterling and Caroline tucked themselves into the coach. Their luggage was strapped on top.

A crack of the whip and the stagecoach was on its way. Yankee Bill was the driver. He knew every turn of the road all the way to Saint Marys.

"We are now crossing the line between Missouri and Iowa," called out Yankee Bill.

The road wound through woodlands of oak, black walnut, and hickory trees in southern Iowa. Sterling admired their beauty.

"I only wish we might find as fine trees as these spread over Nebraska," said Sterling.

"Well, if we do not find them, let's plant them," suggested Caroline.

"Good girl!" exclaimed Sterling. "Whatever

181

we may be or do, we shall be Nebraska tree-planters. There shall be trees wherever we are."

The stagecoach rolled steadily along.

"There is another underground railroad somewhere along here," mused Sterling. "Missouri slaves slip across the line into Iowa and follow an underground railroad."

"Saint Marys in sight," called Yankee Bill.

He brought the stagecoach up to the Iowa House with a flourish.

There from the Iowa bluffs Sterling and Caroline looked across the Missouri River to Bellevue, Nebraska. The Mortons stood quietly watching the fading sunset far out on the Nebraska prairies.

"What a brilliant golden sunset," said Caroline as she stood close to Sterling.

"I hope it means a golden future for you and for me," Sterling spoke softly to his young bride.

Arbor Day

STERLING AND Caroline Morton stepped from the ferry to the soil of Nebraska. They had reached Bellevue, a beautiful spot on the Nebraska bluffs that overlooked the Missouri River.

Peter Sarpy, famous Indian trader and founder of Bellevue, welcomed them. Everyone was cordial and friendly.

"What a truly beautiful view," exclaimed Caroline as she gave a sweeping glance up and down the Missouri.

Everyone was eager to tell of the great future of Nebraska. People were excited as they talked of great things to come.

Sterling had read that Bellevue was the most important port on the Missouri. But other river ports were growing.

Now he listened and talked to people about these other towns. Which were important? What of Nebraska City? That, too, was an important port on the Missouri. What of its future?

Sterling Morton was more eager than ever to be a newspaper man.

Lively changes popped up everywhere.

He plunged into Nebraska politics.

Immediately he became widely known as a political leader.

Important men in Nebraska City became interested in him. Here was a newspaper man of power. Could he be persuaded to come to Nebraska City?

They decided to send a committee to call on him at Bellevue.

"Mr. Morton," said the chairman, "we are here

to invite you to come to Nebraska City as editor of *The Nebraska City News.*"

Sterling Morton was thrilled.

What could mean more to him than this?

Sterling and Caroline knew at once that they must settle in Nebraska City. After only five months in Bellevue they were off to their new home.

The Mortons arrived in Nebraska City on a bright spring day in April. On the high bank of the Missouri they saw the old blockhouse that had once been Fort Kearny.

"See how it commands the river," said Sterling to Caroline. "No river boat could get past the guns on this bluff." But times had changed. Fort Kearney had been moved far to the west.

Long wagon trains moved slowly through the town to settlements far from the Missouri.

The Mortons settled in a modest house on a farm that bordered the town.

Sterling Morton set to work with all his might. Here was his great chance to be a newspaper man.

Here, too, he would become the great tree-planter.

The Nebraska City News gave strong support to the town and to the growth of Nebraska.

Sterling watched every political change.

How he loved a political fight!

He would also be a champion to improve agriculture. He saw in the Nebraska soil a source of great wealth, if he could only help the people see what it could mean if they cared for the soil, cultivated their crops—and planted trees.

Story after story appeared in the *News* telling people how to improve agriculture.

Good seeds and young trees could be brought up the Missouri by river boat.

Sterling Morton practiced what he preached.

He saw the original sod broken on his farm. Then came the cultivation and planting.

Trees, trees, trees! Fine orchards flourished beside broad fields of grain.

Sterling Morton through *The Nebraska City News* planned a local fair. Children were to bring exhibits of the best vegetables they had grown.

Every exhibitor would have his name published in the *News*.

At this first fair there were long ears of yellow corn. Nebraska was a corn country.

Baskets of potatoes meant food for the winter.

Bunches of red beets, yellow carrots, squash, turnips, red and gold tomatoes, and great heads of cabbage showed a land of plenty.

Sterling Morton was becoming somebody by helping everyone to be somebody.

President Buchanan heard of his great leadership and appointed him Secretary of the Territory of Nebraska. For a time he was acting Governor.

All this was before he was thirty years old.

This was before Nebraska became a state.

Sterling Morton was the principal speaker at the First Territorial Fair. He told the people that their great future lay in how they used the good soil.

In the meantime the Morton farm became a beautiful example of Sterling Morton's ideas.

Thousands of trees and flowering shrubs were planted on that farm.

There were orchards of apples, pears, peaches, plums, and cherries.

Surrounding the house were lovely lawns.

Through the years the Morton farm became a fine estate known as Arbor Lodge. Today it is Arbor Lodge State Park.

In a famous speech Sterling Morton said:

"If every farmer in Nebraska will plant out and cultivate an orchard and a flower garden, together with a few forest trees, this will become mentally and morally the best agricultural State, the grandest community of producers in the American Union."

At a meeting of the Horticultural Society in Lincoln, January 4, 1872, Sterling Morton gave a great speech and presented a resolution that he hoped would be accepted.

In this resolution he urged that:

"the 10th day of April, 1872, be . . . set apart and consecrated for tree planting in the State of Nebraska and that the State Board of Agriculture hereby name it Arbor Day . . . and . . . hereby offer a special premium of one hundred dollars to the agricultural society of that county in Nebraska which shall upon that day, plant properly, the largest number of trees; and a farm library of twenty-five dollars' worth of books to that person who, on that day, shall plant properly, in Nebraska, the greatest number of trees."

The people caught the spirit of tree planting. Over one million trees were planted in Nebraska on the first Arbor Day.

Sterling Morton was being somebody in everything he did—in his writing, in his speeches, and in planting trees on his own farm.

In 1885, the state legislature chose April 22, as Arbor Day. It was J. Sterling Morton's birthday. Arbor Day has become a great national idea. It has been so recognized in every state.

Today it is an important day in school systems all over the country. The date must vary in different states because of the differences in climate. School children of America have planted millions of trees. What better things could they have done for themselves and their country.

J. Sterling Morton, too, through his newspaper work and political activities served his country. In 1893, he was appointed Secretary of Agriculture in President Cleveland's cabinet. Mr. Morton was able to work for the development of the farm lands of the nation.

J. Sterling Morton's wisdom led to his being called "The Sage of Arbor Lodge." Each Arbor Day he planted a tree, but in April, 1902, he was unable to do so. On April 22, his seventieth birthday, he was seriously ill, and death came on April 27.

There are statues honoring the man who began Arbor Day, but the trees planted in the past and trees to be planted in the future provide living memorials to J. Sterling Morton.

J. Sterling Morton, through his sense of humor, a touch of mischief, hard work, and determination planted a great idea.

More About This Book

WHEN J. STERLING MORTON LIVED

1832   J. STERLING MORTON WAS BORN IN ADAMS, NEW YORK, APRIL 22.

There were twenty-four states in the Union.

Andrew Jackson was President.

The population of the country was about 13,700,000.

1834   THE MORTON FAMILY MOVED TO MONROE, MICHIGAN.

Samuel Morse invented the telegraph, 1835.

American settlers reached Oregon, 1836.

William Henry Harrison became President and died, 1841.

1846–   MORTON ATTENDED WESLEYAN SEMINARY AND
1854   THE UNIVERSITY OF MICHIGAN.

The Mexican War was fought, 1846-1848.

Elias Howe invented the sewing machine, 1846.

The Mormons reached Great Salt Lake, 1847.

Gold was discovered in California, 1848.

1854   MORTON BECAME A NEWSPAPER MAN AND PO-
LITICAL LEADER IN NEBRASKA.

Lincoln-Douglas debates were held, 1858.

The War between the States was fought, 1861-
1865.

1872   MORTON PROPOSED FIRST ARBOR DAY IN NE-
BRASKA.

Alexander G. Bell invented the telephone, 1876.

The first electric street railway in the United
States was operated in Baltimore, 1885.

1893–   MORTON SERVED AS SECRETARY OF AGRICUL-
1897   TURE IN GROVER CLEVELAND'S CABINET.

Henry Ford built his first gas engine, 1893.

Guglielmo Marconi invented wireless teleg-
raphy, 1895.

1897–   MORTON CONTINUED WORK AS NEWSPAPER
1902   MAN AND POLITICAL LEADER.

The Spanish-American War was fought, 1898.

President William McKinley was assassinated
and Theodore Roosevelt became President,
1901.

1902   J. STERLING MORTON DIED ON APRIL 27.

There were forty-five states in the Union.

194

Theodore Roosevelt was President.

The population of the country was about 77,600,000.

DO YOU REMEMBER?

1. Where did Sterling's parents settle when they moved from Adams, New York?

2. What important lake · was near Sterling's new home?

3. How did Sterling and his friends explore the woods and streams near Monroe?

4. What game did they play to help them identify pieces of cargo on the pier?

5. Why did Mrs. Morton and Sterling go to New York when he was eight years old?

6. How did they travel by boat much of the way to New York?

7. What kind of school did Sterling attend in Monroe?

8. What work did Sterling's Uncle Edward and Grandfather Morton do in Monroe?

9. Where did Sterling hear many exciting stories to tell his friends?

10. What did the boys see when they watched the railroad being built?

11. Where did Sterling go to college and what important things did he do there?

12. What did Morton do after he moved to Nebraska Territory?

13. Why did he recommend establishing Arbor Day in Nebraska?

14. What important cabinet position did he hold under President Cleveland?

IT'S FUN TO LOOK UP THESE THINGS

1. What kind of boats were used in Lake Erie, when Sterling Morton was a boy?

2. When was the Erie Canal completed and who is called the "Father of the Erie Canal"?

3. What happened to William Henry Harrison soon after he became President?

4. When was Nebraska admitted to the Union as a State?

5. Who is Secretary of Agriculture today in the President's cabinet?

6. When does Arbor Day come in your state and who issues a proclamation about it?

INTERESTING THINGS YOU CAN DO

1. Draw a map to show the route Sterling and his mother traveled in going to New York.

2. Make a model or drawing of a railroad train like those used when Sterling was a boy.

3. Prepare a list of different kinds of trees that grow in your part of the country.

4. Make a chart or calendar to show when the different states celebrate Arbor Day. Why do northern states celebrate the day later than southern states?

5. Make a list of foreign countries that celebrate Arbor Day as a day for planting trees.

OTHER BOOKS YOU MAY ENJOY READING

Erie Canal, The, Samuel Hopkins Adams. Trade Edition, Random House. School Edition, Hale.

Robert Fulton: Boy Craftsman, Marguerite Henry. Trade and School Editions, Bobbs-Merrill.

Tecumseh: Shawnee Boy, Augusta Stevenson. Trade and School Editions, Bobbs-Merrill.

Trains, Robert Selph Henry. Bobbs-Merrill.

Trees: A Guide to Familiar American Trees, Herbert S. Zim and Alexander C. Martin. Golden Press.

William Henry Harrison: Young Tippecanoe, Howard Peckham. Trade and School Editions, Bobbs-Merrill.

INTERESTING WORDS IN THIS BOOK

advocate (ăd′vȯ kåt) : person in favor of something

auger (ô′gēr) : tool for boring holes

brogue (brōg) : kind of dialect

cargo (kär′gō) : merchandise carried by a ship

character (kăr′ăk tēr) : symbol or sign that stands for a letter or number

coverlet (kŭv′ēr lĕt) : bedspread

cyclone (sī′klōn) : violent windstorm with the wind blowing in a circular manner

derrick (dĕr′ĭk) : device for lifting heavy weights

198

dignified (dĭg′nĭ fīd) : serious, sedate

discipline (dĭs′ĭ plĭn) : strict behavior

flourish (flûr′ĭsh) : show boldly

generously (jĕn′ēr ŭs lĭ) : liberally

gesture (jĕs′tûr) : use of hand or other part of body to help express or to emphasize an idea

graciously (grā′shŭs lĭ) : in a kindly or courteous manner

hack (hăk) : coach or carriage which may be rented

hawser (hô′zēr) : large rope used to tow or moor a ship

helter-skelter (hĕl′tēr-skĕl′tēr) : in great confusion, disorderly

knuckles (nŭk′′lz) : lumps formed where bones meet in joints, as on the back of the hand

locomotive (lō′kȯ mō′tĭv) : engine that travels under its own power

longshoreman (lŏng′shōr′′măn) : person who works at wharves, loading and unloading ships

militia (mĭ lĭsh′à) : group of citizens organized and trained for public defense, but only called into service in case of emergency

particular (pēr tĭk′ů lēr) : noteworthy, special

199

peninsular (pĕn ĭn′sủ lẽr) : shaped like a peninsula, with land almost surrounded by water

pile (pīl) : long stake or log driven deep into the ground for support

profane (prỏ fān′) : disrespect for God and religion

prominent (prŏm′ĭ nĕnt) : outstanding, notable

proprietor (prỏ prī′ĕ tẽr) : owner or person in control

rancid (răn′sĭd) : having an unpleasant smell or taste

scepter (sĕp′tẽr) : staff carried by a ruler as a symbol of authority

schooner (skōōn′ẽr) : covered wagon used by pioneers on the western prairies

scribbled (skrĭb′′ld) : written hastily or carelessly

stag (stăg) : adult male deer, also descriptive term for men only, as a stag dinner

stout (stout) : strong, tough

sturdy (stûr′dĭ) : hardy, robust

throttle (throt′′l) : valve for controlling the supply of fuel to an engine

yoke (yōk) : bar or frame of wood attached to the necks of two oxen or other animals so that they may be driven or worked as a team